METHUEN'S MONOGRAPHS
ON APPLIED PROBABILITY AND STATISTICS

General Editor: M. S. BARTLETT F.R.S.

The Theory
of Random Clumping

The Theory
of Random Clumping

S. A. ROACH

Reader in Occupational Hygiene
London School of Hygiene and Tropical Medicine

METHUEN & CO LTD
11 NEW FETTER LANE · LONDON EC4

First published 1968
© *S. A. Roach* 1968
Printed in Great Britain by
Spottiswoode, Ballantyne & Co. Ltd.
London and Colchester

Distribution in the U.S.A.
by Barnes & Noble, Inc.

620419

Contents

v

Preface

When objects are scattered at random how many are hidden behind others and how many clumps of two or more will be formed?

This class of problems occurs in such diverse fields as air pollution, astronomy, particle physics and bacterial counting.

In this monograph the theory of random clumping is evolved systematically. The treatment starts with the simplest one-dimensional model and examines the progressive stages leading to the more complex two-dimensional models.

Numerous examples are given of the practical applications of the theoretical results.

The theory is far from complete, but it is hoped that the very lack of answers to so many of the questions will stimulate the reader to produce the solutions.

An attempt has been made throughout to show where the difficulties lie. These may be taken as points of departure for further work in this fascinating area of study.

CHAPTER 1

Introduction

When objects are placed at random some of them overlap to form clumps. A knowledge of the number of the clumps, their size, their shape and the spacing between them helps in the understanding of phenomena in many scientific fields. It would obviously be helpful, for example, to know if clumps have arisen by chance alone or whether there must be an interaction between the elements of an assembly causing a regularity in the spacing between the objects or inducing them to coagulate into compact clumps.

In three-dimensional problems where there is an assembly of objects which interact upon one another through their proximity in space, the properties of the assembly as a whole are largely determined by the interactions between the individual neighbouring members.

The objects may be in size anything from sub-atomic particles to large heavenly bodies which interact due to the forces between the objects. These may be inter-atomic forces, van-der-Waal's forces, electrostatic or magnetic forces, or gravitational forces of attraction.

Through the interaction the assembly may be changing at a steady rate or be unstable or in dynamic equilibrium. In every one of these systems the problem of clumping through chance proximity arises in one guise or another. The interaction varies with the distance apart of the objects. The fields of force around the objects form coherent clumps and it is essential to know the number and size of the clumps which can arise by chance alone. This affects co-operative phenomena of many diverse kinds. For example, on the molecular scale it is a determining factor in the cohesion of matter, the changes of state from gas to liquid to solid and chemical precipitation from a liquid. On the microscopic scale an example is the agglomeration and deposition of the solids in atmospheric pollution, and on the astronomical scale an example is the formation of planetary bodies from matter in space. There are other examples which concern the effect of the assembly on a medium, such as the change in the characteristics of a beam of light when it passes through a solid, a gas or a cloud of dust; the magnetic properties of solid solutions and other materials in a magnetic field, and the percolation of a fluid through a porous solid. All these phenomena depend, in one way or another, upon the coincidence of objects situated at points more or less at random in space.

As might be anticipated, the description of the clumping of objects placed at random on a plane is somewhat simpler than the equivalent problem in three dimensions. Advances have recently been made by workers in the field of industrial hygiene. One of the most important tasks of an industrial hygienist is to determine the concentration of the dust in the air of a work-room.

A variety of different instruments are used in measurements of the concentration of airborne dust. In many of these the method is to collect the dust from a known volume of air and count the number of particles collected with the aid of a microscope. The particles are rarely larger than 0·1 mm diameter, they usually have an irregular shape and some consist of several smaller particles clumped together. It is usually assumed that these clumps were present when the dust was airborne and they are, therefore, counted as single particles. Some of the particles deposited on the sampling plate overlap or completely cover others already deposited. The clumps formed in this way cannot be distinguished from those existing as such in the air and they are also counted as single particles. Consequently, the number of separate airborne particles is underestimated.

Very similar problems occur in bacterial counting. Airborne particles are normally too small to be seen individually with the naked eye and it is difficult to distinguish between organisms and dust particles under the microscope. To determine the number of airborne organisms the airborne particles are collected on a Petri plate coated with a culture medium. In an incubator the viable organisms multiply fast and grow into colonies which are large enough to be counted with the naked eye. The number of distinct colonies which has developed is then counted. Overcrowding of colonies on the plates leads to a biased count as with counting particles.

Curiously, a similar problem occurs in bombing practice. Bombs dropped at random over a target and the number of hits achieved may be determined from the number and size of the distinct craters in the target area.

The equivalent problem in one dimension occurs with machines which count the particles on a sampling plate automatically. The simplest machines for doing this count the number of interruptions to a thin beam of light or electrons as it is traversed across a sample. The number of interruptions is related to the number and size of the particles in the sample. A bias in the count occurs due to the overlapping among the particles. The difference between this problem and the previous ones is that when the beam is much thinner than the particles, the number count is equivalent to the number of distinct marks on a line across the deposit instead of being the number of distinct shapes on a plane. That is, the overlapping is in one dimension only. This effect is enhanced by imperfect resolution in the electrical and optical systems which increases the effective size of the particles. The theory of this problem is simpler than the equivalent two-dimensional one and is closely related to queueing problems which occur in many fields. A near analogy, for example, is found in traffic congestion. Vehicles on the move prevent pedestrians crossing the road in front of them within a distance proportional to their speeds. The number of clumps made up of vehicles closer to one another than this and the size distribution of these clumps determines the waiting time of the pedestrians.

The speed with which a machine counts particles on a sampling plate is generally very fast and the time to count a series is made up mostly with the time taken to fix the sample in the machine and make the machine ready. Another type of machine counts the particles suspended in air or a liquid directly. This is done by passing a thin filament of the fluid through a sensing element, such as a light beam and photomultiplier, or an electric field and capacitor circuit or an electrolyte and current-measuring circuit. The impulses in the electrical circuit are then counted and graded by size by an electronic circuit. The faster the machine samples the air the better the statistical average but the greater is the risk of coincidence between pulses. Machines are designed to count as fast as possible but with a minimum degree of coincidence. Where coincidence errors can be corrected accurately a greater freedom of design is possible.

In health physics instrumentation the coincidence error in counting machines is a well-recognized problem. Radioactive materials disintegrate with time, the disintegrations occurring at random moments. The machines used for counting the rate at which

3

disintegrations occur cannot distinguish between two pulses which occur very close together. This 'dead-time' results in an error in the count which has either to be kept negligible or has to be known accurately so that a correction may be applied.

These examples are sufficient to indicate that the theory of random clumping is needed to procure advances in both theoretical studies and in immediate practical technological problems.

In this monograph it is shown how, with successively simpler models simulating the clumping process, it is possible to get steadily

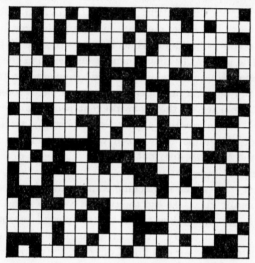

Fig. 1.1. Coincidence on a simple quadratic lattice.

closer to a complete and exact description of the state of clumping. This reduces to an almost purely combinatorial problem with the model illustrated in Fig. 1.1. A number of the squares are filled up at random and the problem is to determine the number of clumps which are formed in doing this. It might be thought that this comparatively simple problem could be solved with ease. However, this problem and similar ones have exercised theoretical physicists for some years and it has not yet been solved.

Interest has centred around the concept of an 'infinite clump'. When there are very few black squares there will be one very large clump of white squares stretching right across the plane. If the dimensions of the plane are infinite this is called an 'infinite' clump. Again, when most of the squares have been filled in, clearly there will be one very large clump of black squares stretching right across the plane. At some critical point, the assembly changes its character when this infinite clump emerges and the infinite clump of white squares vanishes. Suspensions of metal powders are used as conducting paints in the electrical industry. The concentration of metal in the binder of the paint has to be above a critical minimum before the paint becomes conducting. The theory of the change of resistance with concentration is yet another example of the occurrence of an infinite clump, this time in objects of varying size situated at random on a plane. In three-dimensional models the occurrence of an infinite clump at a critical concentration is analogous to a change of state in physics. The way in which the number of objects contributing to the infinite clump subsequently grows with increasing concentration corresponds closely to the behaviour of assemblies in many physical contexts.

One method of attack which has been used to study the infinite clump is to determine the total space taken up by finite clumps and hence by difference deduce the size of the infinite clump. The problem of determining the size and shape of the infinite clump is thus complementary to that of determining the size and shape of the clumps of finite size and the methods used are directly comparable. Results from both approaches are of immediate practical importance, besides having intrinsic theoretical value.

CHAPTER 2

Coincidence in Processions of Black and White

The description of clumping of objects in a one-dimensional model is in every respect simpler than the clumping in two or more dimensions. In addition, it helps in the logical development of the problems in higher dimensions.

The simplest one-dimensional model simulating the coincidence problem is as follows. Firstly, a large number of points are placed in line. Then a proportion selected at random are marked in some distinctive way (Fig. 2.1). Adjacent marked points are then linked,

Squares black or white

Points marked or unmarked

FIG. 2.1. Coincidence in a linear assembly with just two alternatives.

thus transforming the assembly into a number of chains of marked points separated by unmarked points. Alternatively, the problem may be visualized as a procession or single file in which some members are white and the rest black. The black members replace white members chosen at random. This simple example exhibits many of the properties of the more realistic models simulating the clumping process.

The calculation of the expected number of chains is straightforward. A particular member of the procession will be the front member of a chain of black members if, firstly, he is black, probability p, and, secondly, if the member in front of him is white, probability $1-p$.

The probability that a member is at the front of a chain of any number of black members is then

$$p(1-p) \qquad (2.1)$$

6

A single black member with a white member in front and another behind him is included in this and is called a 'chain' of one.

It will be seen later that it is more convenient to develop the results in terms of the density of the black members in the line as a whole. Where N is the mean number of black members in unit length of the line the expected number of chains is

$$N(1-p) \qquad (2.2)$$

Apart from end effects the number of chains of white members must be equal to the number of chains of black members since every white chain is followed by a black one and vice versa.

The 'size' or length of the chains is worked out next. A 'chain' of just one black member is a member who, besides being black, has white members in front and behind him.

Thus in unit length of the line the expected number of black chains of unit length is

$$N(1-p)^2 \qquad (2.3)$$

A member will be at the front of a chain of n black members if firstly he and the $n-1$ members immediately behind him are black, probability p^n, if secondly the nth member behind him is white, probability $1-p$, and if thirdly the member immediately in front of him is white, probability $1-p$.

Thus, combining these, the probability that a member is at the front of a chain of n black members is

$$p^n(1-p)^2 \qquad (2.4)$$

and in unit length of the line the expected number of black chains of length n is

$$C_n = Np^{n-1}(1-p)^2 \qquad (2.5)$$

Further, by adding the chains of length 1, 2, 3... and so on, in unit length of the line the total number of chains,

$$C = N(1-p)^2[1+p+p^2+\ldots] \qquad (2.6)$$

The expression in [ ] brackets is equal to $1/(1-p)$.

Thus $C = N(1-p)$, identical with (2.2). This procedure provides a most useful check in the more complicated models where the total number of chains and the numbers of those of different lengths are obtained by different methods. The results obtained so far are

7

illustrated by the lines in Fig. 2.2. It is supposed that there are 1000 members in unit length of the line. The relationship of the number of these who are black to the number of chains of different length is shown.

It will be noted especially that the curve representing the total number of chains has a single maximum and that given the number of chains there are, in fact, two possible values for the proportion of black members in the procession. To decide which is correct it is

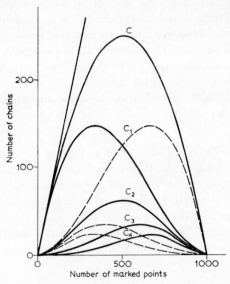

FIG. 2.2. The number of chains, Cn, in a linear assembly with just two alternatives.

necessary to have some additional information, such as the mean length of the chains. This situation corresponds to the property that, whereas at low deposit densities the number counted in a dust sample is small, also with sufficiently high densities overlapping may introduce such a serious bias that most of the gaps between the particles are filled and the number of clumps which are actually separate is also small. In the end the whole sampling plate is covered by one large clump.

The number of chains of length l in the linear assembly is initially very nearly the number of chains of all sizes. With densities below

0·1 the chains of 2 or more account for less than 10% of all chains and less than 20% of all black members.

The size distribution of these chains for three values of p is illustrated in Fig. 2.3. The frequency distributions are discontinuous but very similar to exponential distributions. As the points are brought closer together, in the limit, the probability that an end of a chain occurs in a small element δx of the line is a constant and the size distribution of the chains and also the spaces between them tends to an exponential distribution.

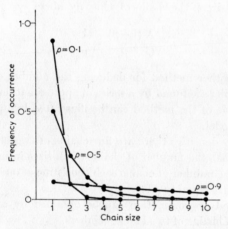

FIG. 2.3. Size frequency distribution of chains in a linear assembly with just two alternatives.

The total number of 'chains' of white members is equal to the total number of chains of black members, but their size frequency distribution is different.

A black member will be in front of a chain of m white members if firstly the m members immediately behind him are white, probability $(1-p)^n$, and if secondly the $m+1$th member behind him is black, probability p.

Thus in unit length of the line the expected number of white chains of length m is

$$C_m = Np(1-p)^m \tag{2.7}$$

This result is illustrated by the family of dotted lines in Fig. 2.2. It will be observed that, as might be expected, the size frequency

2

distribution curves for white chains are reflections of those for black chains about the density 0·5. The complementary nature of the clumps and the spaces between them is found in all models. An examination of the spaces between clumps can often be informative about the size and number of the clumps themselves.

The mean size of the chains of black members,

$$\frac{N}{C} = \frac{1}{1-p} \qquad (2.8)$$

and the mean size of the chains of white members

$$\frac{N(1-p)}{C}\frac{}{p} = \frac{1}{p} \qquad (2.9)$$

There is another method for deducing the number of clumps in which the results are found by a series of approximations.

The principle of the method can be illustrated by applying it to the present model.

At very low densities there are few chains of two or more black members so that the number of chains of all sizes in unit length of the line and the number of chains each consisting of one member are both very nearly equal to N.

An improved approximation can be obtained by correcting for the number of chains of two black members.

The probability that a black member has another black member behind him is p. At low densities the probability that such a pair has white members both in front and behind is very high.

So that to a first approximation the expected number of chains of two black members in unit length of the line is

$$Np \qquad (2.10)$$

Since in each of these chains there are two black members an improved estimate of the number of chains of one member only is

$$N - 2Np \qquad (2.11)$$

and an improved estimate of the total number of chains is given by adding (2.10) and (2.11) giving

$$N - Np \qquad (2.12)$$

By similar reasoning, to a first approximation the expected number of chains of three black members in unit length of the line is

$$Np^2 \qquad (2.13)$$

There are two chains of two members in each chain of three so that an improved estimate may be made of the number of chains of two by correcting for these. By also correcting the previous estimate of the member of chains, each of one member only, the following set is obtained:

$$C_1 = N - 2Np + Np^2 - \ldots$$

$$C_2 = Np - 2Np^2 + \ldots$$

$$C_3 = Np^2 - \ldots$$

$$C = N - Np + \ldots \qquad (2.14)$$

This process can be continued indefinitely. In this way terms are evaluated successively in increasing powers of p.

This method is particularly useful in models where the larger clumps become increasingly difficult to evaluate.

CHAPTER 3

Lines Formed From Short Dashes

The holding periods of a counter start at random times. In a line traverse across a deposit of dust each of the particles which are intercepted cover a small length of the line. These elements, or intercept lengths, may also be likened to dashes placed at random on a line.

The overlapping process in this situation may be visualized as follows.

Dashes are situated with their centres at random points on a line. The dashes overlap one another to form 'clumps' of dashes. The problem is to find the relation between the number of clumps of overlapping dashes and the original number of dashes.

In the solution of this, end effects can be dealt with by adopting one of the following devices:

(i) The line may be made infinitely long and the limiting result obtained when the length of the line approaches infinity (Domb, 1947).

(ii) The line may be made a circle of indefinite radius (Hammersley, 1953). This avoids end effects but raises the possibility of a clump completely encircling the circumference. The limiting result is obtained when the radius of the circle approaches infinity. Other shapes than circular could, of course, be used for this.

(iii) The line may be made of infinite length and the number of clumps determined with ends lying within a finite portion of the line. This is the convention which will be used here. The position of a clump is defined as the position of one of its ends. The left- or right-hand end may, of course, be chosen.

For convenience the word 'clump' will again be used when referring to those consisting of one dash as well as those consisting of several overlapping dashes. It will be called a clump of one dash or a clump of order 1. However, a distinction must now be made between a 'clump' and an 'isolated clump'. Thus in the assembly shown in Fig. 3.1 there are two isolated clumps of three dashes. The isolated

FIG. 3.1. Clumps and isolated clumps.

clump on the left consists of one clump of order 3 (ABC), two clumps of order 2 (AB and BC) and three clumps of order 1 (A, B and C). The isolated clump on the right also consists of one clump of order 3 (ABC), but this time three clumps of order 2 (AB, AC and BC) and three clumps of order 1 (A, B and C). The total number of clumps is thirteen.

The dashes are of length l. The expected number of dashes in unit length is N. A dash to the right of a given dash will overlap the first if it lies within a length l of the first. The expected number of dashes in a length l is Nl and the probability that there are no dashes in length l is

$$\exp(-Nl) \tag{3.1}$$

A dash will be the right-hand member of an isolated clump (of one or more dashes) if no other dash to the right of it overlaps it. Thus the expected number of isolated clumps in unit length of the line, is

$$N\exp(-Nl) \tag{3.2}$$

When the difference between the number of dashes in unit length and the corresponding number of clumps is expressed as a percentage of the number of clumps, it is a measure of the error, R, involved by ignoring the possibility of overlapping.

$$\text{R}\% = 100\frac{(N-C)}{C} = 100[\exp(Nl)-1] \tag{3.3}$$

The error is 100% when $Nl = 0{\cdot}69$. For values of Nl less than $0{\cdot}2$ the percentage error is approximately equal to $100Nl$. To visualize the meaning of the expression Nl it is helpful to remember that it is the combined total length of the dashes in unit length of the line. It is equal to the proportion of the line which would be covered if the dashes were placed end on end.

13

The inverse problem of determining the mean number of dashes deposited in unit length from the mean number of clumps in unit length is slightly more complicated. In expression (3.2) the value of l may be known beforehand, whence N can be found from the equation.

The problem may also be solved by measuring the proportion of the line covered by dashes. A point on the line is *not* covered by a dash if there is no dash within a length l on the line to the right of it. The probability that a point is not covered, P, is thus

$$\exp(-Nl) \tag{3.4}$$

from which the proportion of the line covered by dashes is

$$1 - \exp(-Nl) \tag{3.5}$$

The length of the dashes can also be inferred from the measurements of C and P. Substituting $N = C/P$ (3.5) it is found that

$$l = \frac{-P}{C} \log_e P \tag{3.6}$$

Summarizing the results so far:

Proportion of clumps which are isolated dashes

$$= \exp(-Nl) = P$$

Proportion of line covered by dashes

$$= 1 - \exp(-Nl) = 1 - P$$

Percentage error in the count through overlapping

$$= 100[\exp(Nl) - 1] = 100\left(\frac{1-P}{P}\right)$$

Number of clumps

$$= N \exp(-Nl) = C$$

Length of dashes

$$= l = \frac{-P}{C} \log_e P$$

Mean length of clumps

$$= \frac{\exp(Nl) - 1}{N} = \frac{1-P}{C}$$

The Number of Clumps of n Dashes

The size distribution of the clumps of dashes can be regarded from two points of view. On the one hand one may enquire into the number of clumps that are made up of n dashes in each clump. On the other hand one may also enquire into how many clumps have a length L from end to end irrespective of the number of dashes.

A dash will be isolated if there is no right-hand end of a dash within a length l on either side of its right-hand end. The probability that there is no dash within a portion of length $2l$ of the line is

$$\exp(-2Nl) \tag{3.7}$$

Whence the expected number of isolated dashes in unit length of the line is

$$N \exp(-2Nl) \tag{3.8}$$

The problem next is to determine the expected number of clumps of 2, 3, 4, ... n dashes.

The dashes are situated at random points on the line so that the expected number in any element δy of the line is a constant, equal to $N\,\delta y$, and the probability that a dash lies within the element is independent of the situation elsewhere.

Proceeding from any dash, the next dash to the right of it will overlap it if the interval between them is less than l and will not overlap it if the interval is greater than l.

Starting from a dash chosen at random the process can be regarded as a series of Bernoulli trials. The intervals from one dash to the next on the right represent trials in which a success occurs if the interval is less than l and a failure occurs if the interval is greater than l. The probability of success is equal to the probability that an interval is less than l that is,

$$1 - \exp(-Nl) \tag{3.9}$$

The probability of success in $n-1$ trials, followed by failure in the nth trial, is

$$[1 - \exp(-Nl)]^{n-1} \exp(-Nl) \tag{3.10}$$

A dash is the left-hand member of an isolated clump of n dashes if no other dash to the left of it overlaps it, probability $\exp(-Nl)$, if the $n-1$ dashes in order to the right of it each overlap the preceding

15

one, probability $[1 - \exp(-Nl)]^{n-1}$, and if the nth dash to the right of it does not overlap the $(n-1)$th, probability $\exp(-Nl)$.

Thus, combining these, the probability that a dash is the left-hand member of an isolated clump of n overlapping dashes is

$$\exp(-2Nl)[1 - \exp(-Nl)]^{n-1} \tag{3.11}$$

and in unit length of the line the expected number of isolated clumps of n overlapping dashes, C_n, is

$$N \exp(-2Nl)[1 - \exp(-Nl)^{n-1} \tag{3.12}$$

As a check it may be noted that the total number of dashes is the sum of all the dashes in the individual clumps. That is,

$$N = C_1 + 2C_2 + 3C_3 + 4C_4 + \ldots \tag{3.13}$$

But

$$C_1 + 2C_2 + 3C_3 + \ldots = N \exp(-2Nl)\{1 + 2[1 - \exp(-Nl)]$$
$$+ 3[1 - \exp(Nl)]^2 + \ldots\}$$

from (3.12).

The expression in { } brackets is a binomial series in $[1 - \exp(-Nl)]$ and is equal to $\exp(2Nl)$. Thus

$$C_1 + 2C_2 + 3C_3 = N \exp(-2Nl) \exp(2Nl)$$
$$= N$$

The size distribution is akin to the exponential with the axis at $n = 1$ and for large n this discontinuous distribution tends to the exponential.

The Number of Isolated Clumps of n Dashes and Length L, Dashes all Equal in Length

All 'clumps' of one dash are of equal length l (isolated dashes). Isolated clumps of n overlapping dashes vary in length from l to nl. The problem is to determine the size distribution of the isolated clumps of n dashes in terms of their length, L.

To determine this distribution it is helpful to make a clear distinction between clumps and isolated clumps. Clumps made up of two overlapping dashes may be overlapped by other dashes, but only those which have no other dashes overlapping them are *isolated*

16

clumps of two overlapping dashes. The same applies to clumps of 3, 4, 5 or n dashes.

The required distribution is found by determining firstly the size distribution of the clumps and then the likelihood that they are isolated.

On proceeding to the right from any dash the expected number of dashes in any element, δy, is constant. Consequently the distance from one dash to those others on the right which overlap it has a rectangular frequency distribution with probability density

$$f(y) = 1/l \quad (0 \leqslant y \leqslant l) \tag{3.14}$$

The distances measured between pairs of overlapping dashes are members of a random sample from this rectangular frequency distribution.

The distribution of the sum, s, of $n-1$ of these is required next.

Kendall and Stuart (1963) give the frequency distribution of the mean, m, of a sample of n from a rectangular distribution. The frequency distribution of the sum, s, of a sample of $n-1$, follows by substituting for m

$$m = \frac{s}{l(n-1)}$$

Whence the probability density function of s,

$$f(s) = \frac{1}{l^{n-1}(n-2)!} \sum_{r=0}^{k} (-1) \binom{n-1}{r} (s-rl)^{n-2}$$

$$(kl \leqslant s \leqslant (k+1)l), \, (0 \leqslant k \leqslant n-2) \tag{3.15}$$

k taking integral values only.

Now, the length of a clump is equal to the sum of the distances between the right-hand ends of successive members of the clump together with the length, l, of the first dash of the clump.

Thus, the length, L, of a clump of n dashes is equal to $s+l$ with probability density function for $n=2$ or more

$$f(L) = \frac{1}{l^{n-1}(n-2)!} \sum_{r=0}^{k} (-1)^r \binom{n-1}{r} [L-(r+1)l]^{n-2}$$

$$[(k+1)l \leqslant L \leqslant (k+2)l], \, (0 \leqslant k \leqslant n-2) \tag{3.16}$$

k taking integral values only.

17

The distribution tends to a Normal distribution for high values of n but, as noted by Kendall and Stuart, even for $n=5$ the curve already resembles the Normal closely. The frequency distributions are independent of the density, n, of the dashes. Changes in the density of the dashes alter the relative frequency of clumps of different orders, but the size distribution of the clumps of a given order remains the same. On the other hand the size distribution of *isolated* clumps of a given order does change with density of the dashes.

A given clump of length L will be isolated if there are no other dashes overlapping it. The probability of this is equal to the probability that no dashes lie in a particular length, $L+l$, of the line. This is

$$\exp[-N(L+l)] \tag{3.17}$$

Thus, the frequency distribution of isolated clumps of n dashes of length L has a probability density

$$A\exp[-N(L+l)f(L)] \tag{3.18}$$

A being a constant.

From which,

$$A = \frac{1}{\int_0^\infty \exp[-N(L+l)]f(L)\,dL}$$

$$= \frac{(Nl)^{n-1}}{\exp(-2Nl)[1-\exp(-Nl)]^{n-1}}$$

So that the frequency distribution of isolated clumps of n dashes has the probability density

$$fi(L) = \frac{(Nl)^{n-1}\exp[-N(L+l)]f(L)}{\exp(-2Nl)[1-\exp(-Nl)]^{n-1}}$$

$$= \frac{\exp(Nl).N^{n-1}}{(n-2)![1-\exp(-Nl)]^{n-1}}$$

$$\times \sum_{r=0}^{k}(-1)^r\binom{n-1}{r}[L-(r+1)l]^{n-2}\exp(-Nl) \tag{3.19}$$

Range of L, $[(k+1)l,(k+2)l]$; k, $(0,n-2)$; k taking integral values only.

In terms of the easily measurable parameters C and P this is

$$fi(C) = \frac{1}{P(n-2)!}\left[\frac{C}{P(1-P)}\right]^{n-1}$$

$$\times \sum_{r=0}^{k} (-1)^r \binom{n-1}{r} [L-(r+1)l]^{n-2} \exp(-Nl) \quad (3.20)$$

Range of L, $[(k+1)l,(k+2)l]$; k, $(0,n-2)$; k taking integral values only.

The frequency distributions for isolated clumps of 2 dashes $[fi(L_2)]$, 3 dashes $[fi(L_3)]$, 4 dashes $[fi(L_4)]$ and 5 dashes $[fi(L_5)]$ are given in expanded form below:

$$n = 2; fi(L_2) = \frac{N \exp[N(l-L_2)]}{1-\exp(-Nl)} \qquad \text{range}; (l, 2l)$$

$$n = 3; fi(L_3) = \frac{N^2 \exp[N(l-L_3)]}{[1-\exp(-Nl)]^2}(L_3-l) \qquad (l, 2l)$$

$$\frac{N^2 \exp[N(l-L_3)]}{[1-\exp(-Nl)]^2}[(L_3-l)-2(L_3-2l)] \qquad (2l, 3l)$$

$$n = 4; fi(L_4) = \frac{N^3 \exp[N(l-L_4)]}{2[1-\exp(-Nl)]^3}(L_4-l)^2 \qquad (l, 2l)$$

$$\frac{N^3 \exp[N(l-L_4)]}{2[1-\exp(-Nl)]^3}[(L_4-l)^2-3(L_4-2l)^2] \qquad (2l, 3l)$$

$$\frac{N^3 \exp[N(l-L_4)]}{2[1-\exp(-Nl)]^3}$$

$$\times [(L_4-l)^2-3(L_4-2l)^2+3(L_4-3l)^2] \qquad (3l, \mathbf{4l})$$

$$n = 5; fi(L_5) = \frac{N^4 \exp[N(l-L_5)]}{6[1-\exp(-Nl)]^4}(L_5-l)^3 \qquad (l, 2l)$$

$$\frac{N^4 \exp[N(l-L_5)]}{6[1-\exp(-Nl)]^4}[(L_5-l)^3-4(L_5-2l)^3] \qquad (2l, 3l)$$

$$\frac{N^4 \exp[N(l-L_5)]}{6[1-\exp(-Nl)]^4}$$

$$\times [(L_5-l)^3-4(L_5-2l)^3+6(L_5-3l)^3] \qquad (3l, 4l)$$

$$\frac{N_4 \exp[N(l-L_5)]}{6[1-\exp(-Nl)]^4}[(L_5-l)^3-4(L_5-2l)^3$$

$$+6(L_5-3l)^3-4(L_5-4l)^3] \qquad (4l, 5l)$$

$$(3.21)$$

The frequency distribution curve consists of $n-1$ arcs meeting at the points $L=2l$, $3l$, $4l$, ... $(n-1)l$ where, for $n=4$ or more, there is a common tangent.

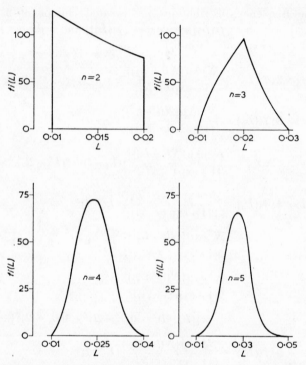

FIG. 3.2. Size frequency distribution ($fi(L)$) of isolated clumps, order n. ($Nl = 0.5$, $l = 0.01$.)

The frequency distributions for $n=2$, 3, 4 and 5 are illustrated in Fig. 3.2. For very large n the distribution becomes more and more skew, tending to a log-Normal distribution. The relationship of the exponential to the log-Normal distribution exhibited by large isolated

20

clumps is identical with the relationship of the rectangular to the Normal distributions exhibited by large clumps without special qualification.

The Total Number of Isolated Clumps, Length L, Dashes all Equal in Length

In unit length of the line the expected number of isolated clumps of n dashes is $N \exp(-2Nl)[1-\exp(-Nl)]^{n-1}$ so that the expected number of isolated clumps of length L, consisting of n dashes, is

$$N \exp(-2Nl)[1-\exp(-Nl)]^{n-1} fi(L) \qquad (3.22)$$

An isolated clump of a given length, L, consists of one dash only if $L=l$. If L lies between $2l$ and $3l$ the isolated clump consists of 3 or more dashes and, in general, if it lies between $(n-1)l$ and nl the clump consists of n or more dashes.

The total number of isolated clumps of 2 or more dashes is

$$N \exp(-Nl)[1-\exp(-Nl)] \qquad (3.23)$$

and from (3.19), (3.22) and (3.23) the frequency distribution of isolated clumps of 2 or more has probability density,

$$fi'(L) = \frac{1}{[1-\exp(-Nl)]} \sum_{n=k+2} \frac{N^{n-1}}{(n-2)!}$$

$$\times \sum_{r=0}^{k} (-1)^r \binom{n-1}{r} [L-(r+1)l]^{n-2} \exp(-Nl)$$

for range of L; $[(k+1)l, (k+2)l]$.

This simplifies to

$$fi'(L) = \frac{N}{[\exp(Nl)-1]} \qquad \text{range; } (L \geqslant l)$$

$$+ \frac{N}{[\exp(Nl)-1]} \sum_{r=1}^{k} (-1)^r \exp(-rNl)$$

$$\times \left\{ \frac{N^{r-1}[L-(r+1)l]^{r-1}}{(r-1)!} + \frac{N^r[L-(r+1)l]^r}{r!} \right\} \quad (L \geqslant (k+1)l)$$

$$(3.24)$$

k taking integral values $(1, 2, 3 \ldots)$ only.

In terms of the easily measurable parameters C and P

$$fi'(L) = \frac{C}{(1-P)} \qquad\qquad \text{range; } (L \geqslant l)$$

$$+ \frac{PC}{(1-P)} \sum_{r=1}^{k} (-1)^r$$

$$\times \left\{ \frac{C^{r-1}[L-(r+1)l]^{r-1}}{(r-1)!} + \frac{C^r[L-(r+1)l]^r}{P.(r)!} \right\} \quad [L \geqslant (k+1)l]$$

$$(3.25)$$

k taking integral values $(1, 2, 3 \ldots)$ only.

The first few arcs of the frequency distribution are given in expanded form below

$$fi'(L) = \frac{N}{[\exp(Nl)-1]} dL \qquad\qquad \text{range; } (l, 2l)$$

$$fi'(L) = \frac{N}{[\exp(Nl)-1]} \{1 - [1 + N(L-2l)]\exp(-Nl)\} dL \quad (2l, 3l)$$

$$fi'(L) = \frac{N}{[\exp(Nl)-1]} \left\{ 1 - [1 + N(L-2l)]\exp(-Nl) \right.$$

$$\left. + [N(L-3l) + \frac{N^2(L-3l)^2}{2!}\exp(-2Nl) \right\} \qquad (3l, 4l)$$

$$fi'(L) = \frac{N}{[\exp(Nl)-1]} \left\{ 1 - [1 + N(L-2l)]\exp(-Nl) \right.$$

$$+ \left[N(L-3l) + \frac{N^2(L-3l)^2}{2!} \right]\exp(-2Nl)$$

$$\left. - \left[\frac{N^2(L-4l)^2}{2!} + \frac{N^3(L-4l)^3}{3!} \right]\exp(-3Nl) \right\} \qquad (4l, 5l)$$

$$(3.26)$$

The form of frequency distribution is interesting and is illustrated in Fig. 3.3 for $Nl = 0.5$ with $l = 0.01$. Between l and $2l$ the frequency is constant as in a rectangular distribution. It will also be noted that this part of the distribution accounts for 77% of the isolated clumps. For lower densities it accounts for even more. So that at low densities the clumps are made up mostly from two sources; one being the isolated clumps and the other being clumps in a rectangular size frequency distribution of lengths between l and $2l$. The ratio of the number of clumps in these two parts is $1/Nl$. The distribution is discontinuous at points $L=l$ and $L=2l$. At $L=3l$ the arcs meet at a point and at $L=Nl$, where n is 4 or more, the arcs meet at a point where there is a common tangent. The arcs are successively of degree 0, 1, 2, 3..., the arc from $L=nl$ to $L=(n+1)l$ being of degree $n-1$.

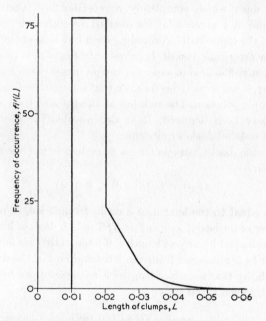

FIG. 3.3. Size frequency distribution $(fi(L))$ of isolated clumps (including all orders) at $Nl = 0.5$, $l = 0.01$.

Dashes of Unequal Length

In the preceding sections a fairly complete description has been obtained of the size distribution of the clumps of overlapping dashes where the dashes are all of equal length. It also seems likely that the solution for dashes of unequal length will be essentially similar, although complicated by embroidery arising from the moments of the parent distribution. However, many abortive attempts made by the author to derive these equations have led him reluctantly to conclude that they cannot be derived in a reasonably short period.

23

This is perhaps a surprising conclusion in view of the comparative ease with which many of the results were derived for dashes of equal length. The difference between the two problems appears to be one of kind rather than degree. With dashes of equal length two successive dashes which do not overlap one another cannot be linked by any other dash, but with dashes of unequal length two successive dashes which do not overlap one another may nevertheless be linked by a preceding dash which completely covers the first. Consequently, the outcome of a given trial for overlap depends not only on the position of the immediately preceding dash but also on the positions of all other preceding dashes. It seems to be impossible to avoid this essentially non-Markovian aspect of the problem.

However, it has already been shown that some parts of the problem have a simple solution. The number of clumps and their mean size have already been deduced. It is also possible to determine the number of isolated dashes quite shortly.

Suppose the dashes vary in length according to the size frequency distribution

$$dF(l) = f(l)\,dl \quad (0 \leqslant l \leqslant \infty) \tag{3.27}$$

where l is equal to the length of a dash. In unit length of the line the number of dashes of length l' is $Nf(l')\,dl'$. A dash of length l will not be overlapped by any of length l' if none of these is located over the length $l+l'$ measured from the left-hand end of the dash. Thus the probability that a dash of length l is not overlapped by any dash of length between l' and $l'+dl'$ is

$$\exp\left[-N(l+l')f(l')\,dl'\right] \tag{3.28}$$

and the probability that this dash is isolated from all others is

$$\prod_0^\infty \exp\left[-N(l+l')f(l')\,dl'\right] = \exp\left[-\int_0^\infty N(l+l')f(l')\,dl'\right]$$

$$= \exp\left[-N(l+\bar{l})\right] \tag{3.29}$$

In unit length of the line the number of dashes of length l if $Nf(l)\,dl$, so that the number of isolated dashes of length l is

$$Nf(l)\exp\left[-N(l+\bar{l})\right]dl$$

and the total number of isolated dashes,

$$C_1 = \int_0^\infty N f(l) \exp\left[-N(l+\bar{l})\right] dl \qquad (3.30)$$

The function $f(l)$ may have a form which enables this expression to be integrated easily. The expression can also be expressed more explicitly and, perhaps, more usefully in terms of the moments of the distribution $dF(l)$. Thus where

$$M_m = \int_0^\infty l^m f(l)\, dl$$

$$C_1 = N \exp(-N\bar{l}) \sum_0 \frac{(-1)^m N^m M_m}{m!} \qquad (3.31)$$

To proceed further will require a determination of the number and size of clumps of order n to set up the conditional probability functions for the number of *isolated* clumps.

The complete solution to this is still not known.

3

CHAPTER 4

Clumps of Laminae in a Plane

A great variety of practical as well as theoretical problems can be resolved into a simple model in which laminae of negligible thickness are located independently at random points on a plane surface.

A cloud of dust particles in a mine, a cloud of metal fume in a foundry and an acid mist in a plating-shop are common air contaminants in our industrial environment. The city dweller inhales air pollution in the form of smoke, fog and smog. Infectious diseases are often carried by airborne organisms embedded in liquid droplets or clumps of dust particles.

Airborne contaminants like these become rapidly mixed with the air by turbulent eddies and deposit by gravity, often aided by centrifugal, thermal and electrostatic forces. The examination of these deposits directly, or the examination of samples collected by instruments, is beset by the difficulties of objects covering or overlapping others.

It is self-evident that photographs of suspension of particles or other objects in liquids, air or outer space also carry with them the problem of resolving those images which overlap.

The problems in the theory of even the simplest two-dimensional model simulating such phenomena seem tantalizingly simple, but in fact few exact solutions have yet been discovered. Even today, an approximate solution to an over-simplified model is the best that mathematics can provide the technologist in this area.

Circular Laminae of Equal Radius Placed at Random in a Plane

Laminae are situated with their centres at random points in a plane. The density is such that the expected number of centres in unit area is N. The laminae are equal circles. Some overlap to form clumps. The problem is to calculate the expected number of separate clumps.

The model is illustrated diagrammatically in Fig. 4.1 which shows a portion of such a plane.

Any two equal circles in a plane will overlap if the distance between their centres is less than the diameter of the circles. From the fact that if the nearest circle to a clump does not overlap it then no other will overlap it, the problem can be transformed into one in the frequency distribution of the distance between a number of points placed at random in a plane.

One of these points is chosen at random as the starting point. A line is drawn from the starting point to the closest other point (see

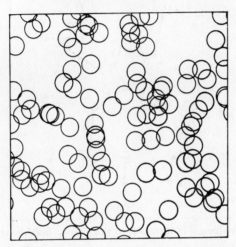

Fig. 4.1. Circular laminae of equal radius place at random on a plane.

Fig. 4.2). Some point is nearer to one of these two than any other. A line is drawn from this third point to whichever of the first two is nearest. Some fourth point is nearer to one of these three than any other. A line is drawn from this point to whichever of the first three is nearest. This process is then continued indefinitely.

It is next supposed that these points are at the centres of circles, radius r.

If the distance, S_1, between the centre of the circle chosen at random and its nearest neighbour is less than $2r$ the circle will be overlapped by its neighbour. Similarly, if the distance, S_2, between the centre of the nearest circle to either of this first pair of circle

27

centres is less than $2r$ then this third circle will overlap one of the
first two. Proceeding next to consider the distance, S_3, between the
centre of the circle which is nearest to one of these three and the
centre of the circle to which it is nearest and so on, the sequence of
intervals, $S_1, S_2, S_3, \ldots S_n$, is obtained. The interval S_i is the distance
from the nearest neighbour of the set of i previous circles to the
centre of the circle of this set to which it is nearest. Thus where the

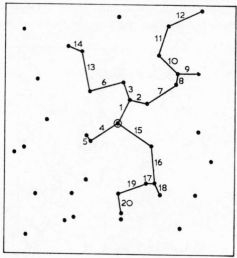

FIG. 4.2. The sequence of intervals to the nearest neighbour of a family.

successive intervals $S_1, S_2, S_3, \ldots S_{n-1}$ are all less than $2r$ the corresponding n laminae form a clump. If, in addition, $S_n \geqslant 2r$ the original
circle, chosen at random, is a member of an isolated clump of n
circles. For instance, with $S_1 < 2r \leqslant S_2$ the circle is a member of an
isolated pair of overlapping circles; that is, an isolated clump of two
circles. Thus, to find the probability that a circle is a member of an
isolated clump of n circles the probability of occurrence of a set of
$n-1$ intervals is required, $S_1, S_2, S_3, \ldots S_{n-1}$, each less than $2r$
followed by an interval $S_n \geqslant 2r$.

Starting from a circle chosen at random this process can be regarded
as a series of trials with success or failure as the outcome. The intervals
from the centre of a circle to its nearest neighbour, from one of these
two centres to the nearest other circle centre and so on, represent

trials in which a success is represented by an interval greater than $2r$ and a failure by an interval less than $2r$.

For a given set of circle centres there is only one set of intervals, which occur in a different order as different centres are taken at random as the starting point. So that the size of the nth interval is very nearly independent of the value of n. This suggests that the probability of success in the nth trial is little different from the probability of success in any other and in particular is little different from the probability of success in the first trial. This gives a method for finding an approximate solution to the model.

The probability p_1 that a circle is isolated is equal to the probability that there is no circle centre within a circle of *radius $2r$* around a point placed at random in the plane. That is,

$$p_1 = \exp(-4\pi r^2 N) \tag{4.1}$$

and the probability that a clump is part of an isolated clump of n laminae,

$$p_n = p_1(1-p_1)^{n-1} \quad \text{(approx.)} \tag{4.2}$$

$$= \exp(-4\pi r^2 N)[1-\exp(-4\pi r^2 N)]^{n-1} \tag{4.3}$$

Since the mean number of laminae deposited in unit area is N, the mean number of isolated clumps in unit area is

$$\frac{Np_n}{n} = \frac{Np_1(1-p_1)^{n-1}}{n} \quad \text{(approx.)} \tag{4.4}$$

Hence the mean number of isolated clumps of all sizes in unit area,

$$C = Np_1\left[1+\frac{(1-p_1)}{2}+\frac{(1-p_1)^2}{3}+\ldots\right] \quad \text{(approx.)}$$

$$= \frac{Np_1\log_e p_1}{p_1-1} \tag{4.5}$$

So that where $p_1 = \exp(-4\pi r^2 N)$

$$C = \frac{4\pi r^2 N^2}{\exp(4\pi r^2 N)-1} \quad \text{(approx.)} \tag{4.6}$$

To test the validity of the initial assumption the number of isolated clumps found by practical experiment can be compared with the number expected from equations (4.3) and (4.6).

29

Points were plotted on square lattices. The lattices were 1000×1000 and the points were plotted at random using six-figure random numbers for the x and y co-ordinates of each point. Circles were drawn with compasses around each of the points as centre. The number of clumps of each size was counted. Where two circles grazed one another and there was doubt of their overlapping the distance between the two circles was checked by direct measurement.

The lattices used were 20 cm $\times$ 20 cm and the circles were 0·5 cm diameter. From 100 to 2000 circles were drawn on each lattice.

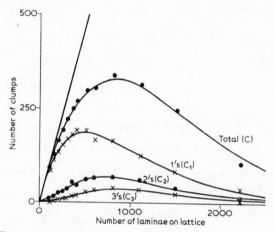

FIG. 4.3. Comparison of the number of isolated clumps expected and the number found by experiment.

Graphs of the number of isolated clumps, doublets, triplets and clumps of all sizes, deduced from equations (4.3) and (4.6), are drawn on Fig. 4.3. The points which appear around these lines are the results obtained from the experiment. It can be seen that the number of clumps counted accords well with the number expected from the assumption of complete independence.

The straight line obtained if the number of clumps were no different from the number of laminae deposited is given for comparison with the other curves. The difference between this line and the curve for the total number of clumps represents the error due to overlapping.

The results are given in more detail in Table 4.1.

TABLE 4.1. The clumps produced by the overlapping of circular laminae on a 1000 × 1000 lattice

No. of laminae on lattice	No. of isolated clumps observed								Total count	
	1's (isolated particles)	2's (doublets)	3's	4's	5's	6's	7's	8's or more	Observed	Expected
100	83	7	1	0	0	0	0	0	91	89
150	111	13	3	1	0	0	0	0	128	129
200	135	25	5	0	0	0	0	0	165	163
250	151	28	10	2	1	0	0	0	192	194
300	170	39	9	2	1	2	0	0	223	220
350	180	54	13	2	3	0	0	0	252	245
400	195	47	18	5	2	2	1	1	271	263
500	191	60	26	10	9	2	2	0	300	294
600	168	68	31	18	12	2	1	5	305	314
800	163	72	40	28	11	7	7	13	341	330
1100	123	64	29	15	19	15	9	39	317	309
1500	83	41	24	18	13	6	4	59	248	246
2220	40	13	7	2	4	1	1	39	107	125

The difference between the last two columns in this table is the difference between the expected number of clumps and the number actually found. The mean difference is not significantly different from zero.

The proportion of the isolated clumps expected in each category was calculated and compared with the number found. The difference was interpreted from a table of the limits of expectation for a Binomial distribution. Out of the sixty-eight results tested it would be expected that three to four results would be found outside the 95% range. There are two outside this range and one border-line case. All three of these results occur in one line of the table, the last, as might be expected, since the columns are correlated with one another.

The agreement between the theoretical and experimental results over the whole range is surprising. This tedious and time-consuming experiment involved the plotting of some 8500 points, drawing circles around them with compasses and counting all the clumps so formed. The lack of any trace of experimental error in the results of such an experiment gives rise to suspicion on two counts.

First, the most important, the agreement of the theory with the form of the experimental results over the very large range of density leaves a strong suspicion that the assumption of independence is far from being a mere rough approximation. Second, the experiment suggests that the variability around the expected results in the absence of experimental error will be considerably less than Binomial.

On the first point it is certain that the value of p_1 is as stated, but it is less certain whether the value of p_n has or has not a steady trend with increasing value of n. On the other hand it will be shown later that at least $p_2 \neq p_1(1-p_1)$.

The test of the agreement between p_n and p_1 for values of n exceeding 2 rests on the comparison with the experimental results. The agreement is so close that for practical purposes the difference is trivial. It is difficult to visualize a steady trend of increasing interval with increasing values of n since any centre may be chosen as the starting point among the unique set of distances. There may perhaps be trends of a cyclic nature, with distances tending to be at one time shorter than average and at another time longer, although there is no evidence for this in the experimental results.

On the second point it is particularly interesting to examine the summit of the curve in Fig. 4.3 representing the total number of clumps, C. At this point on the curve small variations about N give no variation in C. Thus, where deposits have this particular mean density, of N' particles deposited in unit area, different deposits would be expected to contain different numbers of laminae according to a Poisson distribution with mean N' and variance N', but the number of clumps counted in different traverses would not vary at all. Those deposits with low or high densities would reveal just the same number of clumps. Overlapping reduces the variability. Hammersley (1953) also showed how with the one-dimensional problem the variance is lower than Poisson.

In the experiment just described the peak of the curve is near the density at 800 circles on the lattice. In ten adjacent traverses the number of clumps was 38, 36, 32, 36, 33, 32, 29, 37, 33, 35. The mean is 34·1 and the variance is only 7·6.

This suggests that some reduction of variability was indeed taking place in the experiment.

In dust sampling one would not expect to find a sample in which, due to overlapping, the number deposited was greater than, say, 1·5 times the actual number counted. In order to be certain that the formulae would not give biased results the experiments were planned so as to cover a considerably greater range of overlapping than this, for it is at densities exhibiting the greatest overlap where the weaknesses of the approximations show up most clearly. Thus in the last experiment of the series the number of laminae was twenty times the number of clumps counted.

The practical importance of this treatment is that a remarkably good approximation to the number of clumps has been found which can be applied to situations where the density of the laminae is low or high, provided only that the probability that a single lamina is isolated can be calculated or observed experimentally.

Some Other Approximations

Lidwell (1948) calculated the effects of overcrowding on culture plates. Airborne particles are deposited on a Petri plate coated with a culture medium. After incubation the number of colonies is counted by eye. Two or more particles may be deposited so close to one another that, after incubation, only one colony is observed and the count is underestimated. The colonies may grow into one another or, possibly, there may be mutual inhibition of growth. Lidwell assumed that each colony has a constant effective area 'a' and that other particles deposited within the area 'a' will not be distinguished as a separate colony or will not grow owing to inhibition. His treatment followed from the latter assumption. Then, where C is the number of colonies developed, N is the true number of colonies which might have developed and A is the area of the plate;

$$\frac{dC}{dN} = 1 - \frac{Ca}{A} \tag{4.7}$$

from which

$$C = \frac{A}{a}\left[1 - \exp\left(-\frac{Na}{A}\right)\right] \tag{4.8}$$

Lidwell found by comparing thirteen paired samples, one of each pair having twelve times as many particles deposited as the other, that the variation of C with increasing density of deposit followed the above form closely. The assumptions in this treatment may be questioned; the particles are deposited in a few minutes and incubated for 24 hours, the colonies grow steadily in size, they are not of equal area and may merge into one another as they grow. However, the equation developed is of interest as an early attempt to analyse the problem of overlapping.

The data quoted by Lidwell are plotted in Fig. 4.4, together with the curves derived from equation (4.8). It will be noted that the equation gives a curve which is very close to the experimental results.

In Lidwell's colony-counting problem the development and size of a colony may depend upon the proximity of other bacteria carrying particles deposited nearby. In the original deposits of particles, or certainly in the theoretical models which simulate them, the size of the particles themselves is independent of their proximity to others.

The objective in studies of the overlapping in deposits of bacteria or dust is not so often to determine the number of spurious clumps as such as it is to find a working rule for sampling which ensures that the number of such clumps is negligible. For this purpose the simplest of approximations is adequate. The proof that it is adequate is less simple.

For example it is intuitively obvious that when there are few particles on a deposit and overlapping is infrequent, the clumps formed by overlapping will be predominantly clumps of just two particles. That is, clumps of higher orders (3 or more) are negligible by comparison.

To fix ideas it is helpful to consider the model of equal circular laminae placed at random in a plane. In a clump of two overlapping laminae one will be to the left of the other and the number of pairs of overlapping laminae is equal to the number of laminae, each of

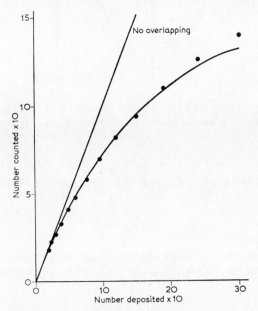

FIG. 4.4. Overlap in bacterial counting.

which has another to the right of it overlapping it. With a lamina radius r, another to the right of it with its centre in the semi-circle of radius $2r$, shown in Fig. 4.5, will overlap it. In unit area the expected number of lamina centres is N. The area of the semi-circle is $2\pi r^2$. So that for small values of N the probability that there is a lamina centre in the semi-circle is very nearly

$$2N\pi r^2 \qquad (4.9)$$

The number of clumps of two overlapping laminae is then

$$2N^2\pi r^2 \qquad (4.10)$$

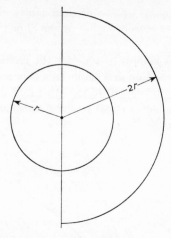

Fig. 4.5. Another lamina centre to the right of a given lamina centre must lie within a distance $2r$ for overlap to occur.

Each of these clumps accounts for two laminae. The number of remaining isolated laminae is then

$$N - 4N^2 \pi r^2 \tag{4.11}$$

The isolated laminae, which will be called clumps of order 1, together with the clumps of two, that is the total number of clumps of order 1 and 2, is thus

$$N(1 - 2N\pi r^2) \tag{4.12}$$

This is a good approximation for small N. The difficulty is that in the absence of an exact formula it is difficult to judge just how good an approximation it really is. Nor is it easy to see whether it over-estimates or underestimates the number which would be counted. For establishing a working rule for practical guidance in sampling, a formula which is known to overestimate the errors due to over-lapping is more useful.

For example, the number of isolated laminae (clumps of order 1) might be evaluated and then the underestimate of C can be deduced by ignoring clumps of two or more. Taking a lamina radius r, any other lying within the circle radius $2r$ shown in Fig. 4.6 will overlap it.

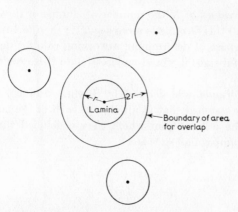

Fig. 4.6. If no lamina lies within a distance $2r$ of a given lamina centre then that lamina will be isolated.

The area of this circle is $4\pi r^2$ so that the probability that a single lamina is isolated is

$$\exp\left(-4N\pi r^2\right) \tag{4.13}$$

and the expected number of single isolated laminae in unit area is

$$N\exp\left(-4N\pi r^2\right) \tag{4.14}$$

This expression is exact for all values of N. Thus, the total number of clumps of all sizes, including the isolated laminae,

$$C > N\exp\left(-4N\pi r^2\right) \tag{4.15}$$

This is a simple approximate formula for C by putting

$$C = N\exp\left(-4N\pi r^2\right)$$

and as such is particularly useful since it is known to underestimate the total number which would in fact be counted. For high densities it grossly underestimates C and ceases to be of much value. A slightly improved estimate of the number of clumps is obtained as follows. Suppose that the laminae not isolated were all in clumps of just two overlapping laminae. Then the number of these clumps of order 2 would be $\frac{1}{2}N[1-\exp(-4N\pi r^2)]$. This overestimates the number of clumps of two or more and, adding the isolated laminae as well, the result

$$C < \tfrac{1}{2}N[1+\exp\left(-4N\pi r^2\right)] \tag{4.16}$$

is obtained.

For small values of N the number of clumps of three or more is negligible and this formula is more accurate than (4.15), but for the practical purpose of determining a working rule for dust sampling it is less useful since it would underestimate the error due to overlapping.

Another formula was derived by Irwin, Armitage and Davies (1948). They assumed that in all clumps each of the laminae overlapped all the others, from which they concluded that the total number of clumps of all sizes is

$$\frac{1-\exp\left(-4N\pi r^2\right)}{4\pi r^2} \qquad (4.17)$$

For very low values of N the clumps consist mainly of isolated laminae and doublets. The number of isolated laminae is exact in the above treatment, but all those laminae with just one other lamina overlapping them are ascribed to doublets. Thus the number of doublets is overestimated and at least for low values of N the formula overestimates the number of clumps. Consequently it underestimates the error due to overlapping and it must be used with caution.

Armitage (1949) made progress in two directions. Firstly he attempted the calculation of the exact number of doublets and triplets for equal circular laminae deposited on a plane and, secondly, he showed how the number of isolated laminae may be deduced when the laminae are of different size or rectangular in shape. His method of deriving the approximations is a little tortuous and need not be considered here, but his recognition of the need to calculate the number of clumps of 1, 2, 3... successively is noteworthy. The salient results obtained by Armitage in this direction can be derived fairly simply using a slightly different method, which illustrates in a simple way how the problems are a mixture of probability, geometry and algebra in almost equal proportions.

For circular laminae, radius r, the expected number of single isolated laminae is given by expression (4.14).

Each clump of two laminae has one lamina centre to the left of the other (Fig. 4.5). The number of doublets is found by determining the number of laminae which are the left-hand members of such pairs. This is done by first establishing the expected number of laminae which overlap a given lamina and then the probability that a given pair is isolated.

The expected number of laminae which are to the right of the first and at a distance x from it is

$$N\pi x\,\delta x \tag{4.18}$$

and the condition for overlap is that x lies between 0 and $2r$.

A given pair will be isolated if no other lamina centre lies within a distance $2r$ of either of the two laminae centres. The outline of this area is shown in Fig. 4.7. This area is

$$4\pi r^2+\frac{x}{2}\sqrt{16r^2-x^2}+8r^2\sin^{-1}\left(\frac{x}{4r}\right) \tag{4.19}$$

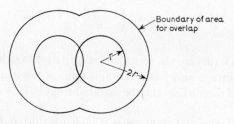

Boundary of area for overlap

FIG. 4.7. The condition for doublets being isolated.

and the probability that no lamina centre lies in this area is

$$\exp\left\{-N\left[4\pi r^2+\frac{x}{2}\sqrt{16r^2-x^2}+8r^2\sin^{-1}\left(\frac{x}{4r}\right)\right]\right\} \tag{4.20}$$

The probability that a given lamina is the left-hand member of an isolated pair of overlapping laminae is therefore

$$\int_0^{2r} N\pi x\,.\exp\left\{-N\left[4\pi r^2+\frac{x}{2}\sqrt{16r^2-x^2}+8r^2\sin^{-1}\left(\frac{x}{4r}\right)\right]\right\}dx \tag{4.21}$$

from (4.18) and (4.20).

This integration is simplified by the substitution, $x=4r\sin(\tfrac{1}{2}\theta)$, which is permissible since x lies between 0 and $2r$. Then

$$dx = 2r\cos(\tfrac{1}{2}\theta)\,d\theta$$

and for the limits; $x(0, 2r)$, substitute $\theta(0, \frac{1}{3}\pi)$. The integral then becomes

$$4N\pi r^2 \int_0^{\pi/3} \sin\theta \exp[-4Nr^2(\sin\theta + \theta + \pi)]\, d\theta \qquad (4.22)$$

This is effectively solved by expanding the terms of the exponential series. A convenient form is, for example,

$$4N\pi r^2 \int_0^{\pi/3} \sin\theta \sum_0 \frac{[-4Nr^2(\sin\theta + \theta + \pi)]^m}{m!}\, d\theta \qquad (4.23)$$

from which the individual terms may be evaluated in increasing powers of $4N\pi r^2$, the density of the laminae on the plane. For example, the first two terms are

$$\tfrac{1}{2}(4N\pi r^2) \quad \text{and} \quad \left(-\frac{3\sqrt{3}}{8\pi} - \frac{1}{2}\right)(4N\pi r^2)^2 \qquad (4.24)$$

respectively.

These two terms are the terms derived by Armitage by his indirect method. Armitage also found the first term of the equivalent series for clumps of three. This may be deduced from the previous working as follows:

Where p_n is the probability that a lamina is the left-hand member of an isolated clump of n

$$p_1 + 2p_2 + 3p_3 + \ldots = 1 \qquad (4.25)$$

But

$$p_3 = A(4N\pi r^2)^3 - \ldots \qquad (4.26)$$

where A is a constant.

Expanding (4.13) in powers of $(4N\pi r^2)$ and substituting in (4.25) together with the results (4.24) it is found that

$$A = \frac{\sqrt{3}}{4\pi} + \frac{1}{6} \qquad (4.27)$$

These results may be summarized as follows. In unit area the number of clumps of

$$\text{order } 1 = N - N(4N\pi r^2) + \frac{N}{2}(4N\pi r^2)^2 - \ldots$$

$$\text{order } 2 = \frac{N}{2}(4N\pi r^2) - N\left(\frac{3\sqrt{3}}{8\pi} + \frac{1}{2}\right)(4N\pi r^2)^2 + \ldots$$

and
$$\text{order } 3 = N\left(\frac{\sqrt{3}}{4\pi}+\frac{1}{6}\right)(4N\pi r^2)^2 - \ldots \qquad (4.28)$$

The total number of clumps is the sum of these, i.e.

$$C = N-\frac{N}{2}(4N\pi r^2)+N\left(\frac{1}{6}-\frac{\sqrt{3}}{8\pi}\right)(4N\pi r^2)^2 - \ldots \qquad (4.29)$$

The complicated terms in expression (4.21) give a hint of the kind of difficulties to be overcome in the exact deduction of the number of

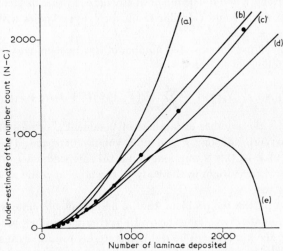

FIG. 4.8. Comparison of approximate formulae for the error in the number count due to overlapping and experimental results.
● Table 4.1   (a) Equation (4.12)   (b) Equation (4.13)
(c) Equation (4.6)   (d) Equation (4.17)   (e) Equation (4.29)

clumps of higher orders. It will emerge later that the problem of stating the probability equations for large clumps is a very formidable one, but to this must be added the burden of increasingly complicated integrations.

Four of the approximate formulae, together with equation (4.6), are compared in Fig. 4.8 where the experimental results discussed in the previous section are plotted. All except equation (4.6) diverge considerably from the experimental results at high densities.

Mack (1954–55) made his contribution by working out the mathematics of isolated laminae and bodies in three-dimensional space

41

where the objects are of different shape or size. Mack studied the geometry of laminae of convex outline and found that in unit area the expected number of isolated laminae,

$$C_1 = \sum_{r=1} N_r \exp\left[-\sum_{u=1} N_u \left(a_u + a_r + \frac{S_u S_r}{2\pi} \right) \right] \qquad (4.30)$$

where N_r is the number of laminae of area a_r and perimeter length S_r in unit area of the plane. That is, he found that for laminae of a given area the number of isolated laminae is dependent only on their perimeter length and independent of any other feature of their shape. Mack also worked out a similar result for convex bodies with three dimensions in space.

In unit volume the expected number of isolated laminae is derived from the following equation:

$$C_1 = \sum_{r=1} N_r \exp\left[-\sum_{n=1} N_u (V_u + A_u P_r + A_r P_u + V_r) \right] \qquad (4.31)$$

where N_r is the number of laminae of volume V_r, surface area A_r, and mean perpendicular P_r, in unit volume of space. The mean perpendicular is the mean length of the perpendicular distance from an arbitrary origin in the body to the tangent plane at a point on the surface.

The first part of the problem, that of finding an adequate working rule for guidance in avoiding the overlap error in counting, was really solved by Mack, although he did not state his results in this form. His general formulae for the number of single isolated laminae can be applied to any assembly. It is an underestimate of the number of clumps which will be counted since clumps of two or more are ignored. Thus, it overestimates the error of overlapping and provides a working rule which errs on the safe side.

Stated explicitly, where R is the percentage error, N is the expected number of laminae in unit area and C_1 is the expected number of single isolated laminae in unit area or single isolated bodies in unit volume,

$$\mathrm{R}\% < \frac{(N - C_1)}{N} . 100 \qquad (4.32)$$

The second part of the problem, that of determining the relationship between the number of laminae or bodies and the number of clumps of all sizes, remains to be solved.

Laminae of Other Shapes

In the laboratory, dust clouds may be produced which consist of spherical particles of approximately equal diameter, but commonly dust clouds consist of particles of irregular shape and of sizes varying from some tens of microns in diameter down to sizes which can just be seen under the microscope. The main effect of the irregular shape of particles is that the more elongated they are the greater is the overlapping. In the extreme, with exceedingly long but very thin particles, each particle overlaps every other one.

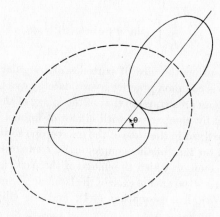

FIG. 4.9. The admissible area around the centre of a lamina within which another lamina centre must lie in order that it shall be overlapped. Elliptical laminae.

Some idea of the magnitude of this effect can be obtained by considering the overlap between elliptical laminae.

The particles are assumed to be ellipses of equal area and equal eccentricity placed at random over a plane with the concentration such that the average number in unit area is N.

A lamina chosen at random will be overlapped by another with its major axis inclined at an angle, θ, to the major axis of the first if the second falls with its centre within the boundary of the dotted curve in Fig. 4.9.

Mack (1954) deduced a general formula for the area enclosed by the locus of the centre of a convex lamina moving around another. Then, taking account of random orientation, he deduced a general formula for the probability that a lamina is isolated. In the present terminology, where the laminae are equal in size, similar in shape and deposited at random points with random orientation,

$$p_1 = \exp\left[-N\left(2a + \frac{s^2}{2\pi}\right)\right] \qquad (4.33)$$

where a is the area of a lamina and s the perimeter length. Now, for ellipses with eccentricity e, Mack's formula can be applied by using the property that $s = 4E\sqrt{ae/\pi}$, where E is the complete elliptic integral,

$$\frac{1}{e}\int_0^{\pi/2} (\sin^2\theta + e^2\cos^2\theta)^{1/2}.d\theta$$

When measuring the size of particles of irregular shape with a microscope it is common practice to estimate by eye the diameter of the circle with an area equal to that of the image of the particle. This is done either by comparison with circles of known diameter on a glass graticule fixed in the tube of the microscope so that its image is superimposed on that of the sample, or by comparison with circles drawn on a screen on which the image of the particles is projected.

Now, where a is the area of each of the laminae, for circular laminae $p_1 = \exp(-4Na)$, from equation (4.1), and for elliptical laminae

$$p_1 = \exp\left[-4Na\left(\frac{1}{2} + \frac{2aE^2}{\pi^2}\right)\right]$$

$$= \exp[-4Nak] \qquad (4.34)$$

from equation (4.33), where k is a constant depending upon the eccentricity of the ellipses.

So that the errors in the number count of elliptical laminae are the same as for circles of a larger area determined by a factor which depends upon the eccentricity of the ellipses.

Corresponding values of e and k were calculated with the help of tables of the complete elliptical integral. These values are given in Table 4.2.

It can be seen from this table that even for laminae as much as twice as long as they are broad ($e=2$) the equivalent circles have an area only 9% greater than that of the ellipses.

44

TABLE 4.2. (See text)

e	1·0	1·2	1·4	1·6	2·0	3·0	5·0	10·0	20·0
k	1·00	1·01	1·02	1·04	1·09	1·25	1·6	2·6	4·6

The result of this is that in calculating the effect of overlapping on the number count, compact particles can be assumed to be equivalent to circular laminae with the same projected area.

As an example, measurements were made of 100 particles, approximately 5 microns in diameter, obtained from sampling the airborne dust at a coal-face while the colliers were digging coal.

The ratio of the longest chord to the breadth measured at right angles to this chord was taken as an indication of the elongation of the particles, which would, if anything, overestimate the equivalent elongation. The average value of this ratio was 1·49. From Table 4.2 it can be seen that with e at this value k is less than 1·03. Thus, in this example, for practical purposes, the irregular outline of the particles may be ignored. In other cases, for example, when the particles are in the form of long fibres or threads, the elongation of the particles cannot be ignored. The airborne dust in factories processing asbestos dust is an example of this. Another model which is more useful in these cases is to assume that the particles are equivalent to lines of length l deposited at random on the plate.

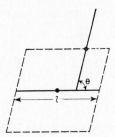

FIG. 4.10. The admissible area around the centre of a line within which another centre must lie in order that it shall be overlapped.

A line chosen at random will be overlapped by another inclined at an angle θ to it if it falls within a rhombus with sides of length l and including angles θ and $\pi - \theta$ (Fig. 4.10). The area of this rhombus is $l^2 \sin \theta$, so that the probability that no other line at any angle, will overlap the chosen line,

$$p_1 = \exp\left[-4 \int_0^{\pi/2} l^2 \sin \theta \cdot \frac{N}{2\pi} \cdot d\theta \right]$$

$$= \exp\left[-\frac{2Nl^2}{\pi} \right] \tag{4.35}$$

Laminae of Unequal Size

The method of evaluating the effects of overlapping among particles of different sizes is illustrated by the case of circular laminae when the size frequency distribution is known to follow some simple law. In determining the general equation for the probability that a lamina is isolated, the method given by Armitage (1949) is followed in outline.

Suppose that the number of laminae in unit area whose diameter lies between δ and $\delta + d\delta$ is $Nf(\delta)d\delta$ $(0 < \delta < \infty)$. Diameter rather than radius is used in this context since it is customary to use this parameter in dust counting.

The probability that a lamina of diameter δ is not overlapped by any lamina of diameter between δ' and $\delta' + d\delta'$ is

$$\exp\left[-\frac{\pi}{4} (\delta + \delta')^2 \, Nf(\delta') \, d\delta' \right] \tag{4.36}$$

The probability that this lamina is not overlapped by any other is therefore

$$\exp\left[-\frac{\pi N}{4} \int_0^\infty (\delta + \delta')^2 f(\delta') \, d\delta' \right] = \exp\left[-\frac{\pi N}{4} (\delta^2 + 2\delta D + V + D^2) \right] \tag{4.37}$$

where D is the mean diameter and V the variance of the distribution of the diameter.

Hence the probability that a lamina is isolated

$$p_1 = \int_0^\infty f(\delta) \exp\left[-\frac{\pi N}{4} (\delta^2 + 2\delta D + V + D^2) \right] d\delta \tag{4.38}$$

This result can then be substituted in equations (4.2) and (4.5) to determine the amount of overlapping since the same reasoning can be applied by defining the nearest neighbour to a clump as the neighbour whose perimeter is nearest to the perimeter of the clump.

The function, $f(\delta)$, may be known accurately from data on the size distribution of the aerosol. If little is known about the exact form of the distribution, or if the integration of equation (4.38) proves to be intractable, then an approximate solution will be required. The size distribution of a sample of dust is often determined by counting the numbers whose sizes lie between those of comparison circles on a microscope graticule and the data from such a determination can be used to solve equation (4.38). In this case

$$p_1 \simeq \sum_{s=0} p_\delta \exp\left[-\frac{\pi N}{4}(\delta^2 + 2\delta D + D^2 + V) \right] \qquad (4.39)$$

where p_δ is the proportion of particles in a small range of sizes whose mid-diameter is δ. If ten ranges are chosen so as to give equal increments in δ^2 then p_1 would be determined with sufficient accuracy for most purposes. This value can then be substituted in equations (4.2) and (4.5) to find the amount of overlapping.

As a practical illustration of the application of the formulae to the situation when p_δ is known to follow a simple law, a useful example is that of the size distribution of the fragments formed by breaking an isotropic substance at random.

If a long stick is broken at points distributed at random then the length of the pieces will be distributed exponentially. More small fragments are produced than large. It is found that when an isotropic material is broken at random the size of the fragments is distributed approximately exponentially (Martin, Blythe and Tongue, 1923–24).

In mining, and in many other industries, a considerable amount of dust is produced by crushing, breaking or grinding hard rock-like materials so that it is expected that the size distribution of the dust will be approximately of exponential form. That is

$$f(\delta) = \frac{1}{D}\exp\left(-\frac{\delta}{D}\right) \qquad (4.40)$$

where D is the mean diameter of the particles. For example, in Fig. 4.11 the results are shown of the determination of the size distribution of ground Pyrex glass dispersed into the air of a small cabinet (approx. 3 ft × 3 ft × 3 ft). The smooth curve through the frequency histogram is the exponential distribution fitted to the data. The mean diameter of the particles, D, is 2·3 microns. It can be seen that the curve is a good fit.

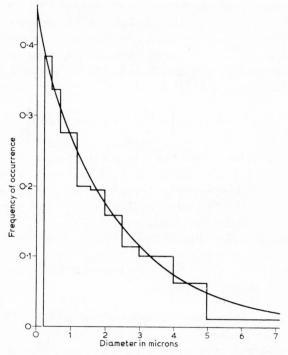

FIG. 4.11. Size distribution of ground Pyrex glass.

Application to Practical Problems of Measurements on Samples of Dust

In a study of the size distribution of the airborne dust in coal-mines, Wynn and Dawes (1951) found that at least in the size range 0·5–10 microns diameter the size distribution does seem to accord with a simple exponential law. The mean diameter of the distribution in these samples was 2·4 microns and most of the samples had a mean diameter between 1·5 and 5·0 microns. Combining (4.38) and (4.40) in one expression

$$p_1 = \int\limits_0^\infty \frac{1}{D}.\exp\left\{-\left[\frac{\pi N\delta^2}{4}+\left(\frac{\pi ND}{2}+\frac{1}{D}\right)\delta+\frac{\pi N}{4}(D^2+V)\right]\right\} \quad (4.41)$$

With the exponential distribution of particle size and rearranging the integral in the standard form of the Normal distribution (4.41) becomes

$$p_1 = \frac{2}{D\sqrt{N}}.\exp\left(1+\frac{1}{\pi D^2 N}-\frac{\pi D^2 N}{4}\right).\int\limits_r^\infty \frac{1}{\sqrt{2\pi}}\exp\left(-\frac{t^2}{2}\right)dt \quad (4.42)$$

where

$$t = \frac{\pi D^2 N+2}{D\sqrt{2\pi N}}$$

The amount of overlapping is then obtained by substituting for p_1 in equation (4.5).

A measure of the error in counting due to overlapping is the proportion of the count, expressed as a percentage, R, which must be added to it to give the number of particles deposited

$$\text{R\%} = \frac{100(N-C)}{C} \quad (4.43)$$

In Table 4.3 the mean number of particles deposited per square millimetre (N) has been calculated corresponding to a number of values of the overlap error (R) on the assumption of an exponential size distribution of the deposited dust, with mean diameter 1·5 microns, 2·4 microns and 5·0 microns respectively.

When applying these results to practical data it should be borne in mind that the exponential distribution of particle diameter is based upon experimental observation and has little theoretical basis to support it. Wynn and Dawes (1951) supposed that, since in one dimension the breaks in an isotropic substance are distributed exponentially, the diameter of the circles of the same projected area as the particles broken from the solid is also distributed exponentially. Such a conclusion requires justification. Moreover, the distribution of products of sample values from exponential distributions is not an exponential distribution. However, distributions similar to the exponential do occur and the simplicity of the exponential has much to commend it for use in analysing dust-sampling results.

So far, consideration has been given to the effect of overlapping on the count of particles of all sizes. However, in some studies only those particles in a restricted range of sizes are of interest. For instance, the concentration of airborne dust of sizes between 1 and 5 microns is used as an index of the risk of pneumoconiosis in the control of dust suppression in British coal-mines (National Coal Board, 1949).

TABLE 4.3. The error due to overlapping with an exponential distribution of the particle diameter (total count)

Error due to over-lapping (%)	Mean diameter of particles (microns)					
	1·5		2·4		5·0	
	No./sq. mm		No./sq. mm		No./sq. mm	
	Deposited	Counted	Deposited	Counted	Deposited	Counted
5	7,800	7,400	3,000	2,900	700	670
10	15,000	13,800	5,900	5,400	1,300	1,200
20	34,000	28,000	13,000	11,000	3,100	2,500
50	104,000	69,000	41,000	27,000	9,400	6,200
100	107,000	85,000	66,000	33,000	15,000	7,600

Clumps are larger than the particles from which they are derived, so that due to overlapping not only is the total count underestimated, but also the mean size of the particles apparently increases.

For laminae of equal diameter, D, the probability, p_0, that a point at random on the plane is isolated, is equal to the probability that there is no lamina centre within a circle radius $D/2$ around the point as centre. That is,

$$p_0 = \exp\left(-\frac{\pi D^2 N}{4}\right) \qquad (4.44)$$

The proportion of the plane covered by laminae is equal to the probability that the point is not isolated, that is, it is equal to $1 - p_0$.

For particles of unequal sizes, suppose that the number of laminae in unit area whose diameter lies between δ and $\delta + d\delta$ is $Nf(\delta)d\delta$ $(0 < \delta < \infty)$.

The probability that a point placed at random in the plane is not overlapped by a lamina of diameter between δ and $\delta + d\delta$ is

$$\exp\left[-\frac{\pi \delta^2 N}{4} . f(\delta)\, d\delta\right] \tag{4.45}$$

The probability, p_0, that the point is not overlapped by any lamina is therefore

$$p_0 = \exp\left[-\frac{\pi}{4}\int_0^\infty \delta^2\, Nf(\delta)\, d\delta\right]$$

$$= \exp\left[-\frac{\pi N}{4}(V + D^2)\right] \tag{4.46}$$

where D is the mean diameter and V the variance of the distribution of the diameter of the laminae.

Where the diameters are distributed exponentially, $V = D^2$ and

$$p_0 = \exp\left(-\tfrac{1}{2}\pi D^2 N\right) \tag{4.47}$$

So that the proportion of the plane covered by laminae,

$$1 - p_0 = 1 - \exp\left(-\tfrac{1}{2}\pi D^2 N\right)$$

and where the number of isolated clumps is C, the mean area covered by an aggregate is

$$\frac{1 - p_0}{C} = \frac{1 - \exp\left(-\tfrac{1}{2}\pi D^2 N\right)}{C} \tag{4.48}$$

An idea can be gained of the magnitude of the effect on the number count of the limited range of sizes by assuming as a first approximation that the size distribution after overlapping remains a reasonably good fit to an exponential distribution. In these circumstances, if D_a is the mean diameter of circles equal in area to the area of the clumps then the mean area of the clumps is $\tfrac{1}{2}\pi D_a^2$; so that, from (4.48)

$$D_a = \sqrt{\frac{2}{\pi C}\left[1 - \exp\left(-\frac{\pi D^2 N}{2}\right)\right]} \tag{4.49}$$

The proportion of particles lying between 1 and 5 microns diameter is

$$\int_1^5 \frac{1}{D} . \exp\left(-\frac{\delta}{D}\right) . d\delta = \exp\left(-\frac{1}{D}\right) - \exp\left(-\frac{5}{D}\right) \tag{4.50}$$

where D is the mean particle diameter in microns.

Corresponding values of the proportion of particles between 1 and 5 microns diameter and the mean diameter are given in Table 4.4, over the range 1·5–6·0 microns mean diameter.

It will be seen that the proportion of particles 1–5 microns varies little with increase in mean diameter over the range 1·5–5·0 microns so that, in practice, it is unlikely that as a result of overlapping the proportion of particles between 1 and 5 microns diameter is altered greatly, and the percentage error in the 1 to 5 microns count is approximately equal to the percentage error in the total count. For example, where the error due to overlapping in the total number count is 100%, and where D is 1·5, 2·4 and 5·0 microns, D_a is 1·8, 2·9 and 6·1 microns respectively (from (4.6), (4.42), (4.43) and (4.49)). Referring to Table 4.4, it will be seen that even under these

TABLE 4.4. The proportion of particles with diameters between 1 and 5 microns, exponential distribution

Mean diameter (μ)	1·5	2·0	2·4	3·0	4·0	5·0	6·0
Proportion 1–5μ	0·48	0·53	0·54	0·53	0·49	0·45	0·40

extreme conditions, for distributions with a mean diameter 2·4 microns there is a negligible change in the proportion of particle with sizes between 1 and 5 microns diameter; for the finest dusts ($D=1·5$) the proportion changes only by about 3% when the error due to overlapping is as much as 100% and for the coarsest dusts ($D=5·0$) the proportion changes only by about 6%.

A number of values of the estimated error in the count 1 to 5 microns is given in Table 4.5.

Considering Table 4.3 and Table 4.5 together, it will be seen that if the sampling is arranged so that there are never more than 1000 particles per sq. mm of all sizes, or 500 particles per sq. mm of particles between 1 and 5 microns diameter, then it is unlikely that the error due to overlapping will exceed 5% except in the occasional very coarse clouds. If the aerosol is known not to be coarse (mean diameter less than 3 microns), it is unlikely that the error due to overlapping will exceed 5% if there are less than 3000 particles per sq. mm of all sizes or 1500 particles per sq. mm of particles between 1 and 5 microns diameter.

If errors greater than 5% can be tolerated the maximum concentration of particles on the deposit may exceed the above levels, to a level roughly in proportion to the error of overlapping.

It should also be noted here, that if some device is used to exclude the coarse particles from the sample then the maximum concentration of particles on the deposit for a given error may be increased, roughly in inverse proportion to the square of the mean diameter of the particles making up the deposit.

TABLE 4.5. The error due to overlapping in the number of particles between 1 and 5 microns diameter with an exponential distribution of particle diameter

Error due to over-lapping (%)	Mean diameter of particles (microns)					
	1·5		2·4		5·0	
	No./sq. mm		No./sq. mm		No./sq. mm	
	Deposited	Counted	Deposited	Counted	Deposited	Counted
5	3,700	3,600	1,650	1,550	310	300
10	7,300	6,600	3,200	2,900	590	540
20	16,000	14,000	7,200	6,000	1,400	1,150
50	51,000	34,000	22,000	14,500	4,200	2,800
100	82,000	41,000	36,000	18,000	6,900	3,400

In some dust-sampling instruments in use at the present time the dust is not deposited evenly. An example of this is the standard thermal precipitator (Green and Watson, 1935; Watson, 1936) which is used to a considerable extent in British coal-mines (Hamilton, Holdsworth and Walton, 1954; Roach, 1955). In this instrument the dust-laden air is drawn into a narrow slit and passes on either side of a hot wire. The heat from the wire deposits the dust on to glass micro-circles fixed on either side of it and the deposits of dust are about 1 cm long and about 1 mm wide. The deposit is uniform in density along its length, parallel to the wire, but it is not uniform across its breadth, at right angles to the wire. To evaluate the amount of overlapping in such a case it is necessary to take account of this non-uniformity in the density of the deposit.

The concentration of particles at different points across one such sample is given in Table 4.6.

The number of particles in successive fields across the deposit was counted, each field being 0·08 mm square, so that 437 particles were counted, in a traverse of total length 1·6 mm and width 0·08 mm.

TABLE 4.6. The frequency of occurrence of particles in a traverse at right angles to a thermal precipitator deposit

Field	No. counted	% in field
1	0	0
2	1	0·2
3	5	1·1
4	6	1·4
5	14	3·2
6	20	4·6
7	31	7·1
8	67	15·4
9	75	17·2
10	87	19·9
11	60	13·7
12	32	7·3
13	16	3·7
14	8	1·8
15	8	1·8
16	3	0·7
17	1	0·2
18	2	0·5
19	1	0·2
20	0	0
Total	437	100·0

To calculate the amount of overlapping in such a case it is necessary to take account of the changing density of the deposit, since there will be disproportionately more overlapping at the centre where there are more particles than towards the edges.

Assuming that the density of the deposit is uniform in the length of each field (0·08 mm), the number of particles that would be counted and the overall error due to overlapping are given in Table 4.7 for exponential distributions of particle size with mean diameters 1·5,

2·4 and 5·0 microns respectively. The counts are referred to a traverse of 0·03 mm (30 microns) wide since this is the width that is most commonly used.

It will be seen that under the assumptions of the calculations, namely that the size distribution of the deposited dust follows the simple exponential law and that the particles deposit in positions independently of one another, then the error due to overlapping will usually be less than 5% provided that there are fewer than fifty

TABLE 4.7. The estimated error due to overlapping, counting a thermal precipitator sample of airborne coal dust. (Counts are given corresponding to a traverse width of 0·03 mm)

Error due to over-lapping (%)	Mean diameter of particles (microns)					
	1·5		2·4		5·0	
	Number count		Number count		Number count	
	Total	1–5μ	Total	1–5μ	Total	1–5μ
5	135	65	50	27	12	6
10	270	125	100	55	24	11
20	660	320	200	110	50	22
50	2000	960	730	390	180	80
100	3600	1700	1300	700	320	150

particles of all sizes on each traverse or less than twenty-five particles of sizes 1–5 microns.

It is probable that in practice a greater concentration than this would be necessary before an overlap error of 5% is attained, since only a small proportion of those particles in excess of 20 microns diameter are deposited by this instrument and, in addition, it is usually found in examining thermal precipitator deposits that there is a slight tendency for the finer particles to be situated to one side of the deposit. Both these factors would tend to reduce the error due to overlapping.

It is also possible that the particles do not deposit independently of one another since the thermal gradient between the hot wire and the depositing surface, which effects the deposition, may be influenced locally by the particles already deposited. Further, in the deposition of the dust from the air by the hot wire it is unlikely that the particles approach the depositing surface in a path exactly at right angles to it and the effective area of a particle, equal to the area of its 'shadow' on the depositing surface, is increased. For these reasons the figures given in Table 4.7 for this instrument should be treated with some caution.

The error due to overlapping on thermal precipitator samples has been measured experimentally from a comparison of counts of pairs of samples in which one sample of each pair was five times as dense as the other (Roach, 1958). Two thermal precipitators were set up side by side in a colliery. Pairs of samples were then taken in which one of the instruments sampled for five times as long as the other. Each short-period sample was taken during the middle of the corresponding sample taken by the long-period instrument.

One hundred and twenty-five such pairs of samples were taken so as to include a wide variety of dust concentrations. The particles counted on the long-period samples were less than five times those on the short-period samples because of the overlapping. The data were fitted to the equation:

$$C = N \exp(-aN)$$

The mean value for a was 0·0017 for the total number count and 0·0032 for the count 1–5 microns. This corresponds to an overlap error of 5% when the total number count is thirty particles per 30 microns traverse width or when the count 1–5 microns is sixteen particles per 30 microns traverse width. The results in Table 4.7 suggest the mean diameter of the particles was about 3·7 microns.

Ashford, Dodgson, Hadden, Skorobohatyj and Fay (1963) measured the amount of overlapping in thermal precipitator sampling by arranging two dust deposits to intersect in the form of a cross. By comparing the count at the intersection with counts on the arms of the cross a measure of the error due to overlapping at the centre was obtained. Their results, repeated in many British coal-mines, suggested that the mean diameter of the particles used by Roach was 3·3 microns.

Their own data, referring only to the count 1–5 microns, is summarized in the regression line:

$$N = C + D^2(0{\cdot}0002078C^2 + 0{\cdot}000003748C^3)$$

This equation agrees with Table 4.7 for errors up to 10% but suggests greater overlap error at higher counts. This may be because their values of mean diameter referred to the apparent size, which, at high deposit densities, is raised because of overlapping. There is no reason to doubt their equation is appropriate when based upon the value of D measured on the overcrowded sample.

Circular Laminae of Equal Radius. Exact Formulae

If the radius of the laminae is known the number on the plane can be calculated from the area of the plane covered by laminae.

It was shown in equation (4.44), that the proportion of the plane covered by laminae,

$$1 - p_0 = 1 - \exp\left(-\pi r^2 N\right)$$

So that by counting the isolated clumps and measuring their mean area p_0 can be calculated, from which

$$N = \frac{1}{\pi r^2} . \log_e\left(\frac{1}{p_0}\right) \qquad (4.51)$$

Where the laminae are of unequal radius, the equivalent formula is

$$N = \frac{1}{\pi(r^2 + v)} . \log_e\left(\frac{1}{p_0}\right) \qquad (4.52)$$

where v is the variance of the distribution and r the mean radius of the laminae, from equation (4.46).

In practice neither the mean radius of the particles nor the variance of the radius is known very precisely and at densities sufficiently low for these to be assessed with accuracy from the samples themselves the approximate formulae already available are good enough for deducing the number deposited. At high densities a formula is required whose parameters can be determined from the size of the clumps as they exist in the sample, not the size of the particles from which they are derived.

The Number of Clumps of n Laminae

The mathematics required in the exact solution of equations for the number of clumps of more than three circular laminae is peculiarly intractable. This halts progress before the associated combinatorial problems become complicated.

5

In what follows, the distinction between clumps and isolated clumps should be kept in mind. Isolated clumps are only a fraction of all the clumps.

$n = 1$

Each lamina is a clump of 1 lamina so that the expected number of clumps of 1 lamina is equal to N.

$n = 2$

Each clump of 2 laminae has one lamina centre to the left of the other (Fig. 4.5). A lamina is the left-hand member of a clump of two if another lamina with its centre to the right of the first overlaps it.

All laminae within a distance $2r$ of a given lamina centre overlap the lamina. Thus the expected number of laminae to the right of the first and overlapping it is equal to the expected number in a semi-circle radius $2r$. This is $2N\pi r^2$. Thus the expected number of clumps of two laminae for which a given lamina is the left-hand end is

$$2N\pi r^2 \tag{4.53}$$

and the expected number of clumps of two laminae in unit area of the plane is

$$2N^2\pi r^2 \tag{4.54}$$

$n = 3$

A lamina situated within a distance $2r$ of another will overlap it. A third may overlap both of these or just one of them to make a clump of three laminae. Thus a lamina, centre A, will be overlapped by another lamina, centre B, if $AB < 2r$. A third lamina, centre C, will overlap both the first two if C lies in the common area of circles radius $2r$ about A and B. This is shown in Fig. 4.12.

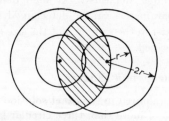

FIG. 4.12. When there are two overlapping laminae a third will overlap both if its centre lies in the shaded area.

This area is

$$4\pi r^2 - \frac{x}{2}\sqrt{16r^2 - x^2} - 8r^2 \sin^{-1}\left(\frac{x}{4r}\right), \ (AB = x) \qquad (4.55)$$

The expected number of laminae a distance x from a given lamina is

$$2N\pi x\, \delta x$$

The number of pairs of centres such as B with C whose laminae overlap A is thus

$$2N^2\pi\left[4\pi r^2 x - \frac{x}{2}\sqrt{16r^2 - x^2} - 8r^2 x \sin^{-1}\left(\frac{x}{4r}\right)\right]\delta x \qquad (4.56)$$

The total number of such pairs, where x takes any value between 0 and $2r$, is thus

$$2N^2\pi\int_0^{2r}\left[4\pi r^2 x - \frac{x^2}{2}\cdot\sqrt{16r^2 - x^2} - 8r^2 x \sin^{-1}\left(\frac{x}{4r}\right)\right]dx$$

Substituting $x = 4r\sin(\tfrac{1}{2}\theta)$, $dx = 2r\cos(\tfrac{1}{2}\theta)\,d\theta$, and for the limits $x;\,(0,2r)$ substituting $\theta;\,(0,\tfrac{1}{3}\pi)$, the integral becomes

$$32N^2\pi r^4\int_0^{\pi/3}\sin\theta(\pi - \theta - \sin\theta)\,d\theta = 16N^2\pi r^4\left(\pi - \frac{3\sqrt{3}}{4}\right) \qquad (4.57)$$

The set of three such laminae making up a given clump of three mutually overlapping laminae may be counted in any order given by the permutations of the three. There are six of these so that the number of distinct clumps of three of this kind in unit area is

$$\tfrac{2}{3}N^3\pi r^4(4\pi - 3\sqrt{3}) \qquad (4.58)$$

The third lamina centre will overlap just one of the first two if it lies in the unshaded portion of Fig. 4.19. This area is

$$x\sqrt{16r^2 - x^2} + 16r^2\sin^{-1}\left(\frac{x}{2r}\right) \qquad (4.59)$$

The number of pairs B and C of this kind is

$$2N^2\pi\int_0^{2r}\left[x^2\sqrt{16r^2 - x^2} + 16r^2\sin^{-1}\left(\frac{x}{2r}\right)\right]dx = 24N^2\pi r^4\sqrt{3} \qquad (4.60)$$

using the same substitution.

A set of three laminae making up a given clump of this kind may be counted in any of four orders ABC, BAC, BCA, CBA. The number of distinct clumps of three of this kind in unit area is thus

$$6N^3 \pi r^4 \sqrt{3} \tag{4.61}$$

From (4.58) and (4.61) the total number of clumps of three is therefore

$$N^3 \pi r^4 (\tfrac{8}{3}\pi + 4\sqrt{3}) \tag{4.62}$$

n = 4 or more

The geometry of four or more overlapping circles is so complicated that the integrations become excessively burdensome before any hope of a general solution for clumps of n emerges.

Square Laminae, Aligned Parallel, Situated at Random Points in a Plane

The laminae are situated with their centres at random points on a plane. They are equal squares of side-length, l, and are aligned with their sides parallel. A portion of such a plane is illustrated in Fig. 4.13. In unit area the expected number of laminae is N. The problem is to determine the number of isolated clumps.

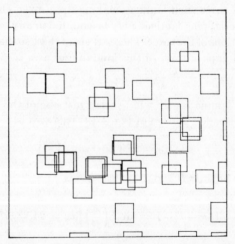

FIG. 4.13. Square laminae aligned parallel situated at random in a plane.

Edge effects are avoided by restricting attention to a symmetrical convex area of the plane and by counting those clumps which do not touch any part of the edge of the left of the area.

In the previous section on circles an analysis was used based on a consideration of the distances between points placed at random on a plane. The formulae derived were demonstrably not exact but their inexactness was so slight as to be insignificant in practice. In this section a model has been chosen with which an exact treatment is described. The mathematics is more complicated but as it deals with exact statements it is perhaps more satisfying.

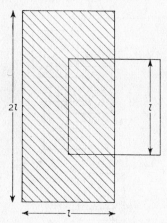

FIG. 4.14. A square lamina will be a left-hand end if no lamina centre lies in the shaded area.

First a left-hand end of an isolated clump is defined as a lamina with no other lamina which is on the left of it overlapping it.

A lamina will be a left-hand end if there are no lamina centres in the shaded area in Fig. 4.14. This has an area $2l^2$. The probability that there are no laminae in an area $2l^2$ is $\exp(-2Nl^2)$. The number of clumps, C, is approximately equal to the number of left-hand ends, E_1 (Mack, 1955). Thus in unit area the expected number of clumps,

$$C \simeq N \exp(-2Nl^2) \qquad (4.63)$$

In one-dimensional cases there is only one left-hand end to each clump and the number of clumps is exactly equal to the number of left-hand ends. However, in all two-dimensional models (and higher dimensions) a clump may have more than one left-hand end. So that, to be exact, with two-dimensional models

$$C < E_1 \tag{4.64}$$

that is, $C < N \exp(-2Nl^2)$, when the laminae are parallel squares.

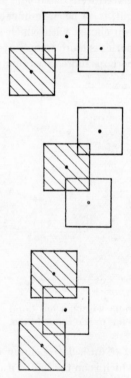

FIG. 4.15. Clumps of three laminae. Left-hand ends shaded.

This inequality can be reduced by taking account of the number of ends to a clump.

In the clumps of three laminae shown in Fig. 4.15 the last has two left-hand ends. The clump with two ends forms an open-ended chain with the central lamina to the right of both the others. A clump of three has two left-hand ends if one of the laminae is overlapped by two others to the left of it, which do not themselves overlap each other. Also, it will be noted that such a lamina is not a left-hand end.

This suggests that a correction may be made by calculating the number of such laminae. In large clumps there may be more than two left-hand ends. A clump usually has $m+1$ left-hand ends if it contains m laminae which are each overlapped on the left by just two others which do not overlap each other. Examples are given in the accompanying diagram (Fig. 4.16).

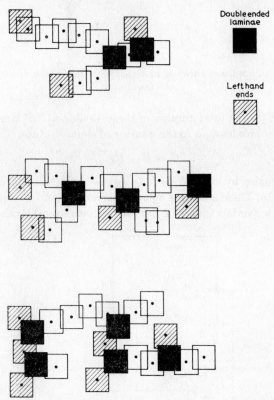

FIG. 4.16. Clumps with laminae leading to double ends.

It will be appreciated that with this model no more than two left-hand ends can stem from one lamina. With other models, more than two left-hand ends can be produced. For example, with laminae of equal circles, 1, 2 or 3 ends may stem from one lamina and for circular laminae of different size many small ones may be bunched on the perimeter of a large one, making many ends (see Fig. 4.17).

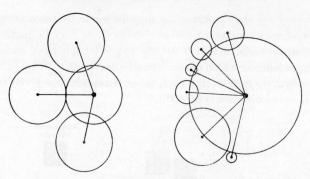

FIG. 4.17. Examples of three or more separate laminae branching from
one lamina.

Where E_2 is the total number of these 'double-ended' laminae an
improved approximation to the number of clumps is thus

$$C \simeq E_1 - E_2 \qquad (4.65)$$

The reasoning by which E_2 is deduced may be followed by examining Fig. 4.18. There are three equal squares A, B and C. Squares B
and C both overlap square A but do not overlap each other. The

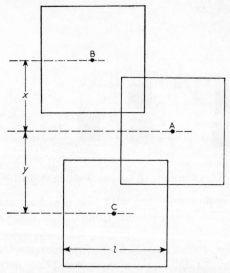

FIG. 4.18. Conditions for a double-ended lamina.

centres of squares B and C are both to the left of the centre of A. It follows that the centre of square B cannot lie below the horizontal line through A. Where x is the vertical distance of the centre of square B from this line and y is the vertical distance of the centre of square C from this line, the range of x is $(0,l)$ and the range of y is $(l-x,l)$. Since squares B and C both overlap A, both the centres of these squares must lie within a distance l measured horizontally; this distance being measured to a vertical line through the centre of square A.

Between x and $x+\delta x$ the centre of square B must thus lie somewhere in an area $l\,\delta x$, and between y and $y+\delta y$ the centre of square C must lie somewhere in an area $l\,\delta y$.

Where square A represents a square chosen at random on the plane, the probability that there is another square, B, is an area $l\,\delta x$ is

$$Nl\,\delta x$$

The area within which the centre of a square must lie if it is to overlap square A between B and C is, horizontally, width l and, vertically, height $x+y$. The probability that there is no centre in this area is

$$\exp-Nl(x+y)$$

So that the probability that A is a double-ended square with B at distance x and C at distance y is

$$Nl^2\exp-Nl(x+y)\,\delta x\,\delta y \tag{4.66}$$

and the probability that A is double-ended is

$$\int_0^l\int_{l-x}^l N^2l^2\exp-Nl(x+y)\,dx\,dy \tag{4.67}$$

so that

$$E_2 = N\int_0^l\int_{l-x}^l N^2l^2\exp-Nl(x+y)\,dx\,dy \tag{4.68}$$

The integral is evaluated and it is found that

$$E_2 = N[Nl^2+\exp(-Nl^2)-1]\exp(-Nl^2) \tag{4.69}$$

65

From this, a further improved approximation for the number of clumps is

$$C \simeq E_1 - E_2 \qquad (4.70)$$

i.e.

$$C \simeq N(1 - Nl^2)\exp(-Nl^2) \qquad (4.71)$$

That the approximation (4.70) does not give the exact solution is readily apparent from the solution itself. All values of Nl^2 greater than 1 yield a negative result. This equation underestimates the number of clumps for values of Nl^2 greater than at most 1. There must be some other factor still unaccounted for.

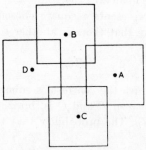

FIG. 4.19. Laminae in rings.

This other factor is first observed in one of the possible arrangements of a clump of four laminae. This arrangement is shown in Fig. 4.19. This clump has one 'double-ended' square A, yet only one left-hand end, square D. The extra left-hand end yielded by A, through B and C, has become absorbed by D, thus making a complete circle. More complicated cases of this are illustrated by Fig. 4.20. The number of 'double-ended' squares which yield an extra left-hand end is in fact diminished by the number of completely enclosed areas or islands within the clumps. Where the number of these areas within each clump is I and the total are counted, $\sum I$, then the number of clumps is given exactly by the equation

$$C = E_1 - E_2 + \sum I \qquad (4.72)$$

From which

$$C > E_1 - E_2 \qquad (4.73)$$

i.e.

$$C > N(1 - Nl^2)\exp(-Nl^2) \qquad (4.74)$$

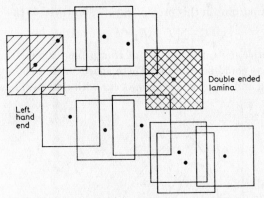

Double ended lamina

Left hand end

FIG. 4.20.

It will be shown in the next section that the expected number of isolated laminae in unit area is $N \exp(-4Nl^2)$. The number of clumps is greater than the number of isolated laminae. So that, from (4.64), limits of C may be given thus:

$$C_1 < C < E_1 \qquad (4.75)$$

That is,

$$N \exp(-4Nl^2) < C < N \exp(-2Nl^2) \qquad (4.76)$$

Also from (4.73) and (4.75)

$$E_1 - E_2 < C < E_1 \qquad (4.77)$$

that is,

$$N(1 - Nl^2) \exp(-Nl^2) < C < N \exp(-2Nl^2) \qquad (4.78)$$

When

$$1 - Nl^2 = \exp(-3Nl^2)$$

$$C_1 = E_1 - E_2$$

At values of Nl^2 less than this (4.78) gives closer limits than (4.76). At values of Nl^2 greater than this (4.76) gives closer limits than (4.78).

These limits can be compared with the accurate formula given in equation (4.5) by substituting $p_1 = \exp(-4Nl^2)$. The four curves are illustrated in Fig. 4.21 for $l^2 = 0.01$. It will be seen that C_1 is an accurate estimate of C for values of Nl^2 up to 0·1, E_1 is an accurate estimate of C for values of Nl^2 up to 0·2 and $E_1 - E_2$ is an accurate estimate of C for values of Nl^2 up to 0·4. Beyond this point the curves begin to diverge markedly.

More important in this present review, however, is the conclusion

$$C - \sum I = E_1 - E_2 \quad \text{exactly.} \tag{4.79}$$

In practice, both the number of clumps and the number of these island areas could be counted. These spaces within clumps are very rarely seen and in any case cannot occur with clumps of less than four

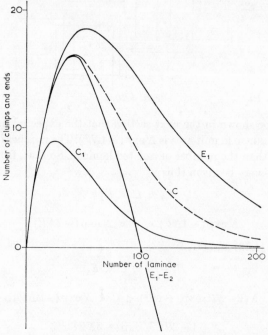

FIG. 4.21. Upper and lower bounds for the expected number of isolated clumps. N.B.: $I + C - (E_1 - E_2)$.

in this model or clumps of less than at least three for other models. This equation shows, that by modifying the counting procedure so as to include an assessment of spaces wholly within clumps a satisfying exact formula may be calculated from which to derive the true number deposited. The mathematical requirements are limited to the definable properties of individual laminae expressed in the factors E_1 and E_2, instead of being spread over analytical geometry whose complexity increases without limit as larger and larger clumps are considered. Of these two factors, E_1 is by far the easiest to deduce.

The other factor, E_2, is the number of extra left-hand ends yielded by a lamina through other overlapping laminae (thus allowing for those cases admitting more than two ends from one lamina).

It is more involved than E_1 but is resolvable through geometry and algebra in a limited length of time.

Before proceeding further it is interesting to note a particular result from the model so far considered.

When $Nl^2 = 1$, $E_1 - E_2 = 0$, that is $C = \sum I$. The number of clumps is exactly equal to the number of spaces wholly within clumps when Nl^2 is unity.

The significance of this remarkable property at this particular concentration is not readily apparent. Experiment shows that these spaces are much smaller than the clumps in which they lie. Nl^2 is the sum area of the individual laminae. It may be that in all models, at this area concentration, when Nl^2 or its equivalent is unity, the number of spaces within clumps is equal to the number of clumps. It is also conceivable that when $Nl^2 = 1$ an infinite clump emerges. This clump, if it exists, contains an infinite number of spaces wholly enclosed. Proceeding along its perimeter from lamina to lamina the path taken is equally likely to turn left or right. This condition also holds when the number of spaces is equal to the number of clumps.

The Number of Isolated Clumps of *n* Laminae

$n = 1$

A lamina is isolated if no other lamina centre lies within a distance l measured vertically or horizontally from its centre. This area is a square, side length $2l$ (see Fig. 4.22). The probability that there are no lamina centres in an area $4l^2$ is,

$$\exp(-4Nl^2) \qquad (4.80)$$

which is equal to the probability that a chosen lamina is isolated.

The expected number of isolated laminae in unit area of the plane is thus

$$N \exp(-4Nl^2) \qquad (4.81)$$

$n = 2$

69

In Fig. 4.23 is shown a clump of two overlapping square lamina

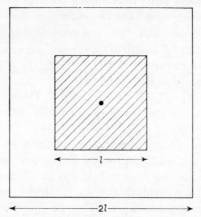

FIG. 4.22. The admissible area within which a lamina must lie to overlap a given lamina.

centres A and B. This pair is isolated if no other lamina centre lies within a horizontal or vertical distance l of either A or B. The area covered by this condition is outlined in the figure (cf. Fig. 4.7). Where A is the origin, and the position of B from A is measured in

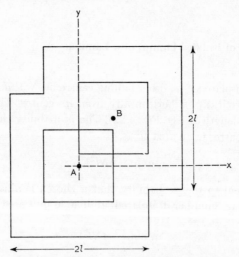

FIG. 4.23. Calculation of the number of isolated doublets (see Text).

rectangular co-ordinates (x, y), taking Ax as the horizontal, then this area is

$$8l^2 - (2l - x)(2l - \bar{y}) \tag{4.82}$$

in which $\bar{y}$ is the absolute value of y.

Each isolated clump of two overlapping laminae has just one left-hand end. For the square with centre B to overlap the square with centre A and remain to the right of it, x must lie between 0 and l, and y must lie between $-l$ and $+l$. The number of laminae which are the left-hand ends of isolated clumps of two overlapping dashes can now be determined.

Taking the centre of a lamina chosen at random in the plane as A, then the probability that another lamina centre B, lies between x and $x + \delta x$, and between y and $y + \delta y$, is $N \delta x \delta y$.

The probability that no other square overlaps either of these two is

$$\exp \{ -N[8l^2 - (2l - x)(2l - \bar{y})] \} \tag{4.83}$$

The probability of occurrence of a particular isolated pair of overlapping laminae AB is thus

$$N \exp \{ -N[8l^2 - (2l - x)(2l - \bar{y})] \} \, \delta x \, \delta y \tag{4.84}$$

and the probability that the particular lamina centre A is the left-hand end of an isolated pair of overlapping laminae is

$$\int_0^l \int_{-l}^l N \exp \{ -N[8l^2 - (2l - x)(2l - \bar{y})] \} \, dx \, dy$$

$$= \int_0^l \int_0^l 2N \exp \{ -N[8l^2 - (2l - x)(2l - y)] \} \, dx \, dy \tag{4.85}$$

Using the substitutions $u = 2l - x$ and $v = 2l - y$ this simplifies to

$$2N \exp(-8Nl^2) \int_{2l}^l \int_{2l}^l \exp(Nuv) \, du \, dv$$

$$= 2 \exp(-8Nl^2) \int_{2l}^l \frac{\exp(Nlu) - \exp(2Nlu)}{u} \cdot du$$

This may be evaluated from the result that

$$\int \frac{\exp(ax)}{x} \, dx = \log_e x + \frac{ax}{1!} + \frac{a^2 x^2}{2.2!} + \frac{a^3 x^3}{3.3!} + \cdots$$

Hence

$$\int_{2l}^{l} \frac{\exp(Nlu) - \exp(2Nlu)}{u} \, du$$

$$= \frac{Nl^2}{1!} + \frac{3^2}{2.2!} (Nl^2)^2 + \frac{7^2}{3.3!} (Nl^2)^3 + \frac{15^2}{4.4!} (Nl^2)^4 + \cdots \quad (4.86)$$

From this, the probability that a lamina is the left-hand end of an isolated pair of overlapping laminae is

$$2Nl^2 \exp(-8Nl^2) \sum_{r=1} \frac{(2^r - 1)^2}{r.r!} . (Nl^2)^{r-1} \quad (4.87)$$

So that the expected number of isolated clumps of two overlapping squares is

$$2N_2 l^2 \exp(-8Nl^2) \sum_{r=1} \frac{(2^r - 1)^2}{r.r!} . (Nl^2)^{r-1} \quad (4.88)$$

The first few terms of this series, expressed as a series in powers of Nl^2, is

$$N \left[2Nl^2 - \frac{23}{2} (Nl^2)^2 + \frac{281}{9} (Nl^2)^3 - \frac{9437}{144} (Nl^2)^4 + \frac{87,533}{900} (Nl^2)^5 - \cdots \right]$$

$$(4.89)$$

The geometry of clumps of three is still quite straightforward, but the integration of the expressions to derive explicit formula for the number of clumps is very cumbersome. That is, the bar to further progress with this model is simply one of tedious algebra.

CHAPTER 5

Coincidence of Random Points on a Square Lattice

It has been shown in the earlier sections that by progressively simplifying the models a method emerges for determining the number deposited from the number of clumps and holes in the deposit. The other parameter of practical importance is the size distribution of the particles. By analogy with the one-dimensional problems it seems hardly likely that this can be derived without a knowledge of the number of clumps of n laminae for all values of n. The evaluation of clumps of order n with n increasing stepwise, $1, 2, 3 \ldots$, has progressed further with each simplification of the model. However, no systematic algebraic pattern has yet emerged and the possibility of one emerging seems remote. Possibly some important features of the problem are obscured by the remaining element of integration. An examination of even simpler models which avoid calculus therefore seems worthwhile.

The laminae are placed at random points on a lattice (Fig. 1.1). In the simplest case only adjacent laminae overlap. That is, clumps are formed by linking only those laminae whose centres are on the immediately adjacent points either horizontally or vertically. It will be appreciated that given the solution for this model the situation for laminae placed at random on a plane can be approached by progressively increasing the range of points around a given centre which become linked to it. However, even the simplest model presents formidable difficulties.

The Number of Clumps and Isolated Clumps

In a square lattice the probability that a point is marked is p. Clumps are formed by linking all marked points which are adjacent either horizontally or vertically. The problem is to determine the expected

73

number of clumps in unit area when the expected number of marked points is N in unit area.

It is first necessary to define the end of a clump so that then the number of clumps can be examined by determining the number of points which have the appropriate conditions to be these ends. As in the earlier models a clump may have many left-hand ends. Attention is therefore focused on the extreme left-hand ends. Further, to

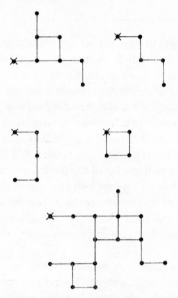

FIG. 5.1. The 'end' of a clump is the uppermost extreme left-hand end (marked X).

allow for the possibility of several such extreme left-hand ends from one clump being on the same vertical, the 'end' of a clump is defined as the uppermost of those ends which lie on the extreme left-hand vertical passing through the clump (Fig. 5.1).

In this model, the overlapping process is so elementary that little extra clarity is given by examining in detail the number of clumps before determining the number of those clumps which are isolated. The process has been so simplified that it is mainly a combinatorial exercise and the object will be to determine the number of isolated clumps directly.

As in earlier sections the number of left-hand ends is determined first. On a square lattice, a left-hand end is defined as a marked point with the point on its immediate left unmarked and the point above it unmarked. The probability that a point is unmarked is q. Normally $q = 1 - p$ but this equality will only be used at the finish so that the results obtained on the way can also be applied to other related problems when $q \neq 1 - p$. For example, the points may be marked in several different colours and those clumps surrounded by particular alternatives may be required.

The expected number of left-hand ends in unit area of the lattice is thus

$$E_1 = Nq^2 \tag{5.1}$$

The number of double-ended marked points also may be determined, just as the number of double-ended laminae were determined in previous sections.

No more than two left-hand ends can stem from one marked point in a square lattice. A marked point is a double-ended marked point if the point immediately to the left of it is marked and if also the point immediately above it is marked.

The expected number of double-ended marked points in unit area of the lattice is thus

$$E_2 = Np^2$$

A marked point will be isolated if the four immediately adjacent points around it are unmarked. Thus, the expected number of isolated marked points in unit area of the lattice

$$C = Nq^4 \tag{5.2}$$

Upper and lower limits may now be given to the number of isolated clumps, C

Thus, $$C_1 < C < E_1 \tag{5.3}$$

that is $$Nq^4 < C < Nq^2 \tag{5.4}$$

and $$E_1 - E_2 < C < E_1 \tag{5.5}$$

that is $$N(q^2 - p^2) < C < Nq^2 \tag{5.6}$$

These limits for C are illustrated in Fig. 5.2 for unit area containing 100 points of the lattice. Then, $p = N/100$. Also q is assumed equal to $1 - p$.

An improved estimate can be made of the number of isolated clumps by taking into account some of the holes wholly within clumps. The simplest kind is a square made up of four linked marked points. By choosing, say, the upper left-hand point of the square as its end, then

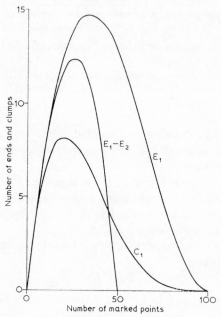

FIG. 5.2. Clumping on a square lattice. Limits of the number of isolated clumps, C.

the number of such squares is found by calculating the expected number of points which form the top left-hand corner of such a square. This is

$$Np^3 \tag{5.7}$$

A further improvement again may be made by taking into account larger holes wholly within clumps. The next largest is a square made up of eight marked points with the centre square unmarked. The expected number of these is

$$Np^7q \tag{5.8}$$

Thus

$$E_1 - E_2 + Np^4 + Np^7q < C < E_1 \tag{5.9}$$

76

That is

$$N(q^2 - p^2 + p^3 + p^7 q) < C < Nq^2 \tag{5.10}$$

Still further improvements require an examination of the number of yet larger holes; this leads to problems akin to those for finding the number of isolated clumps of order n. However, it will be noted

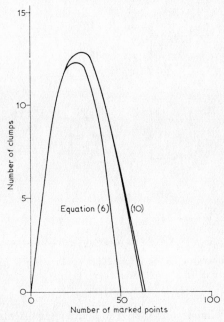

Fig. 5.3. Improvements to the lower bound of C.

that a hole larger than one surrounded by eight marked points must be derived from a clump of order 10 or more. So that provided these are few in number the estimate will be an accurate one.

The three steps to this stage are illustrated in Fig. 5.3 for unit area containing 100 points of the lattice, assuming q is equal to $1-p$. It will be observed that the improvement between stages two and three is already marginal. Further improvements cease to be worth the effort required to achieve them.

The Number of Isolated Clumps of n Laminae

The position of an isolated clump is defined as the position of its uppermost extreme left-hand end. Advantage may be taken of topologically identical clumps as follows.

The eight clumps of four linked marked points shown in Fig. 5.4 are topologically identical. They can be recognized by eye as being

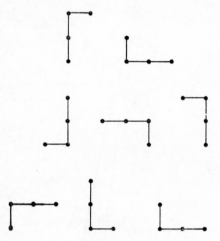

FIG. 5.4. Eight combinations of four linked points which are topologically identical.

geometrically similar but placed in a different orientation relative to the origin. That is, they are made up of different combinations of marked points which are equally likely to occur. All the orientations may be produced from any one of them by reflection either through one or through two of the three planes which are perpendicular to the plane of the lattice and coincident with its horizontal, vertical and diagonal axes. With the square lattice, depending on their symmetry, there may be 1, 2, 4 or 8 distinct clumps which are topologically identical.

By considering all the possible combinations of marked points the number of topologically distinct clumps, n_t, may be found.

For $n = 1$ to 7 these are as follows in Table 5.1.

TABLE 5.1. The number of topologically distinct clumps, n_t. Square lattice

	n_t	n_t with the following number of orientations:			
		1	2	4	8
$n = 1$	1	1	0	0	0
$n = 2$	1	0	1	0	0
$n = 3$	2	0	1	1	0
$n = 4$	5	1	1	2	1
$n = 5$	12	1	1	5	5
$n = 6$	35	0	2	13	20
$n = 7$	108	0	4	20	84

By studying the shape of their perimeters the number of unmarked points required to isolate them may be found.

From this the expected number of isolated clumps of order n follows.

In practice this becomes a very time-consuming task as n increases in size. The results for n, 1 to 7, work out as follows:

$$C_1 = Nq^4$$
$$C_2 = Npq^5(2q)$$
$$C_3 = Np^2q^6(4q+2q^2)$$
$$C_4 = Np^3q^7(9q+8q^2+2q^3)$$
$$C_5 = Np^4q^8(1+20q+28q^2+12q^3+2q^4)$$
$$C_6 = Np^5q^9(4+54q+80q^2+60q^3+16q^4+2q^5)$$
$$C_7 = Np^6q^{10}(22+136q+252q^2+228q^3+100q^4+20q^5+2q^6) \quad (5.11)$$

Putting $q=1-p$ then for terms up to Np^6 the summation

$$C_1+C_2+\ldots C_7 = N(q^2-p^2+p^3)$$
$$= E_1-E_2+Np^3 \quad (5.12)$$

As a further check it may be verified that

$$C_1+2C_2+3C_3+\ldots 7C_7 = N$$

for terms up to Np^6. The results for C_1, C_2, C_3 and C_4 are plotted in Fig. 5.5.

This process for finding and checking the results of C_n becomes rapidly very laborious and there is again little hope of a systematic progression emerging in a short time. Domb *et al.* (1960) were concerned with the mean clump size and determined an expression for this which included two further terms for the mean clump size beyond Np^6. They also gave the results of similar studies with other lattices.

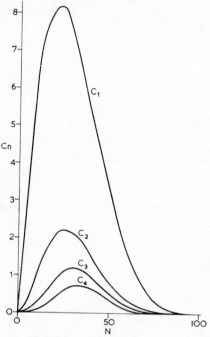

FIG. 5.5. The number of clumps of marked points (C_n) on a square lattice of 100 points.

It will have been noticed that with each simplification of the models used in this monograph more and more progress was possible, although none, so far, has progressed to the point where an exact answer either to the total number of clumps of all sizes or their size distribution was possible. As long as there is no solution for the simplest models there is no hope for discovering a method for solving the more complicated models.

Before leaving the square lattice it will perhaps be informative to consider the progress made in narrowing the limits for C, even though the exact value of C has not been found. Equations (5.11) may be summed to provide a lower bound for C. An upper bound may also be derived from them by assuming that the marked points not

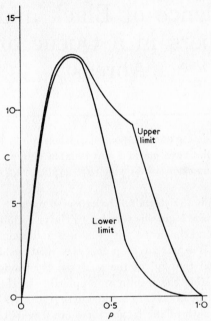

FIG. 5.6. Rigorous limits for the number of clumps on a square lattice of 100 points.

accounted for by equations (5.11) are all taken up by clumps of eight marked points. Thus

$$C_1 + C_2 + \ldots C_7$$
$$< C < C_1 + C_2 + \ldots C_7 + \left[\frac{N - (C_1 + 2C_2 + 3C_3 + \ldots 7C_7)}{8} \right] \quad (5.13)$$

For values of p below 0·57 equation (5.9) provides a greater lower bound for C than does equation (5.13). Also, for values of p above 0·62 equation (5.9) provides a smaller upper bound for C than does equation (5.13). Taking this into account the narrowest limits for C are exemplified by taking $q = 1 - p$ and unit area 100 points, illustrated in Fig. 5.6. It will be observed that these rigorous upper and lower bounds, although locating C within a narrow band for $p < 0·4$, do not provide very satisfactory limits for C much greater than 0·4.

81

CHAPTER 6

Coincidence of Black and White Members in a Queue of Two Abreast

In a lattice consisting of $m \times n$ points, width m points, length n points, some of the points are marked and isolated clumps are formed by linking all the marked points which are adjacent either horizontally or vertically.

The problem is to determine the expected number and size of the clumps, where $m = 2$ and n is very large. The probability that a point is marked is p and the probability that it is unmarked is q.

Normally q is equal to $1 - p$ but this relationship will not be introduced until the end of the analysis. By leaving q as an independent variable the results are applicable to the more general problem where the points are marked in several ways.

Along the length of the lattice there are n pairs of points. Each pair of points may have both of its points marked, both unmarked, or one marked and one unmarked, with probabilities p^2, q^2 and $2pq$ respectively.

The model is illustrated in Fig. 6.1. In Fig. 6.2 is presented the division of pairs of points into the three kinds. When p is near zero

FIG. 6.1. Marked points on a $2 \times n$ lattice.

most of the pairs of points are unmarked. When $p = 0.5$, one-quarter of the pairs have both points marked, one-quarter have both points unmarked and the remainder have one marked and one unmarked. When p is near unity most of the pairs of points are marked.

Aligning the lattice with its length horizontal, a pair of points, both of which are marked, will be at the left-hand end of an isolated clump if the adjacent pair of points to the left are both unmarked, probability q^2. If only one of the points of the pair is marked it will be at the left-hand end of a clump if the adjacent point to the left of it is unmarked, probability q.

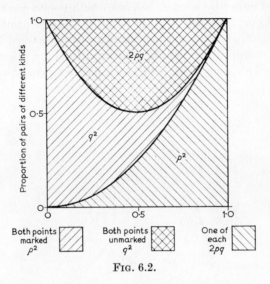

FIG. 6.2.

The probability that a pair of points is at the left-hand end of a clump is thus

$$p^2q^2 + 2pq^2 \qquad (6.1)$$

and the total number of clumps is

$$n(p^2q^2 + 2pq^2) \qquad (6.2)$$

The result is illustrated in Fig. 6.3 (the uppermost line) which has been drawn with scales for a lattice of 100 points, that is fifty pairs of marked points. It may be compared with Fig. 2.2, which shows the equivalent one-dimensional result. It will be noted that the curve for the total number of clumps has become skew by introducing two dimensions.

It remains to determine the size distribution of the clumps.

Choose a clump at random, start from the left-hand end and move to the right. In doing this, let the probability that a set of s consecutive pairs of points are all linked together be P_s. Some of these

83

sets have at the right-hand end a single marked point, probability P'_s, say, and the remainder have at the right-hand end a pair of marked points, probability P''_s $(=P_s-P'_s)$.

A pair of points, both marked, is linked to the next pair on the right if followed either by another pair with both points marked (probability p^2) or by a pair with any one of the two points marked (probability $2pq$). Where only one point of a pair is marked it is linked to the next pair on the right if followed either by a pair with both points marked (probability p^2) or by a pair with the point marked

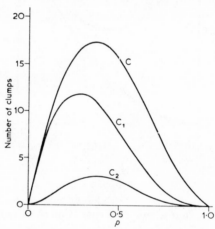

FIG. 6.3. Number of clumps per 100 points of a $2 \times n$ lattice.

which is on the same horizon as the preceding marked point (probability pq). Thus

$$P''_{s+1} = p^2(P'_s+P''_s) \tag{6.3}$$

$$= p^2 P_s \tag{6.4}$$

and

$$P'_{s+1} = pq(P'_s+2P''_s) \tag{6.5}$$

$$= pq(P_s+p^2 P_{s-1}) \tag{6.6}$$

i.e.

$$P_{s+1} = (pq+p^2)P_s+p^3qP_{s-1} \tag{6.7}$$

This is a linear difference equation in P_s, with constant coefficients and may be solved by standard methods. Thus, its auxiliary equation is

$$x^2-(pq+p^2)x-p^3q = 0 \tag{6.8}$$

whose roots are

$$\frac{pq+p^2 \pm p\sqrt{p^2+q^2+6pq}}{2}$$

so that the general solution is

$$P_s = \frac{A_1(pq+p^2+p\sqrt{p^2+q^2+6pq})^s + A_2(pq+p^2-p\sqrt{p^2+q^2+6pq})^s}{2^s}$$

(6.9)

where A_1 and A_2 are arbitrary constants.

All sets have at least one pair of points, that is,

$$P_1 = 1$$

So that

$$P_1' = \frac{2}{2+p} \quad \text{and} \quad P_1'' = \frac{p}{2+p}$$

Substituting these values in (6.3) and (6.5), then

$$P_2 = p^2 + \frac{2pq(1+p)}{2+p}$$

(6.10)

By substituting these results for P_1 and P_2 in the equation for P_s it is possible to solve for A_1 and A_2. Then,

$$A_1 = \frac{2(2q+2pq+2p+p^2)-(2+p)(p+q-\sqrt{p^2+q^2+6pq})}{p(2+p)(p+q+\sqrt{p^2+q^2+6pq})\sqrt{p^2+q^2+6pq}}$$

(6.11)

and

$$A_2 = \frac{(2+p)(p+q+\sqrt{p^2+q^2+6pq})-2(2p+2q+2pq+p^2)}{p(2+p)(p+q-\sqrt{p^2+q^2+6pq})\sqrt{p^2+q^2+6pq}}$$

(6.12)

So that

$$P_s = \{[2(2p+2q+2pq+p^2)-(2+p)(p+q-\sqrt{p^2+q^2+6pq})]$$

$$\times (p+q+\sqrt{p^2+q^2+6pq})^{s-1} - [2(2p+2q+2pq+p^2)$$

$$-(2+p)(p+q+\sqrt{p^2+q^2+6pq})](p+q-\sqrt{p^2+q^2+6pq})^{s-1}\}$$

$$\div [2^s p^{1-s}(2+p)\sqrt{p^3+q^2+6pq}]$$

(6.13)

85

The probability that the chosen clump is of length s is equal to the probability that s pairs of points are linked together and are not linked to the $s+1$th pair. This is

$$q^2 P_s'' + q P_s'$$

which from (6.4) and (6.5) is equal to

$$(p^2 q^2 + pq^2) P_{s-1} + p^3 q^2 P_{s-2} \tag{6.14}$$

The total number of clumps is $npq^2(2+p)$ so that the number of clumps of length s is,

$$np^2 q^4 (2+p)[(1+p)P_{s-1} + p^2 P_{s-2}], \quad (s = 3 \text{ or more}) \tag{6.15}$$

For $s=1$ the number of clumps is

$$npq^3(2+p) \tag{6.16}$$

and for $s=2$ the number of clumps is

$$np^2 q^4 (2 + 2p + p^2) \tag{6.17}$$

These curves are also illustrated in Fig. 6.3.

In clumps of length s the number of marked points varies between s and $2s$. Where the number of marked points is t the number of unmarked points is $2s-t$. In addition, beyond the clump, to the left and to the right, there are two pairs of points, in each of which there is either one or two unmarked points opposite the ends of the clump. So that the number of clumps, length s, consisting of t marked points is

$$np^t q^{2s-t+2}(a + bq + cq^2) \tag{6.18}$$

where a, b and c are functions of s and t. On the other hand, substituting for P_s in (6.15) and expanding the expression obtained it is found that the coefficient of p^t is

$$nq^{2s-t+2}\left\{ 2\sum_r \left[\binom{s-2-r}{r}\binom{s-2-2r}{2s-2-t-r} + \binom{s-3-r}{r}\binom{s-3-2r}{2s-2-t-r} \right] \right.$$

$$+ 4q\sum_r \left[\binom{s-2-r}{r}\binom{s-2-2r}{2s-1-t-r} \right]$$

$$\left. + q^2 \sum_r \left[\binom{s-2-r}{r}\binom{s-2-2r}{2s-t-r} + \binom{s-3-r}{r}\binom{s-3-2r}{2s-1-t-r} \right] \right\}$$

$$s \leqslant t \leqslant 2s \tag{6.19}$$

It follows that

$$a = 2 \sum_{r} \left[\binom{s-2-r}{r} \binom{s-2-2r}{2s-2-t-r} + \binom{s-3-r}{r} \binom{s-3-2r}{2s-2-t-r} \right]$$

(6.20)

$$b = 4 \sum_{r} \left[\binom{s-2-r}{r} \binom{s-2-2r}{2s-1-t-r} \right]$$

(6.21)

and

$$c = \sum_{r} \left[\binom{s-2-r}{r} \binom{s-2-2r}{2s-t-r} + \binom{s-3-r}{r} \binom{s-3-2r}{2s-1-t-r} \right]$$

(6.22)

The parameters of equation (6.18), given explicitly in equations (6.20), (6.21) and (6.22), are sums of simple products of binomial coefficients. Their evaluation is either by reference to a table of binomial coefficients or by direct calculation.

As an example, clumps of length 10 ($s = 10$) have been evaluated. The parameters a, b and c are given in Table 6.1. The number of marked points, t, in these clumps varies from 10 to 20. The size frequency distribution of the clumps (length 10) is calculated by applying equation (6.18) for each value of t. The frequency distributions when $p = 0.2$, 0.5 and 0.8, and $q = 1 - p$, are given in Fig. 6.4. As might be

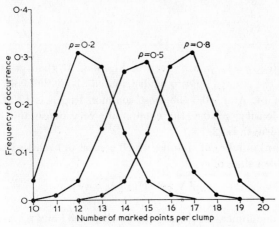

FIG. 6.4. Frequency distribution of the number of marked points per clump for clumps of length 10 in a quadratic lattice $2 \times \infty$.

expected at the lower densities ($p=0.2$) the clumps are thinnest and contain a minimum of marked points for a given length. At $p=0.2$ the most common number of marked points for clumps of length 10 is 12, at $p=0.5$ the most common number is 15 and at $p=0.8$ the most common number is 17.

As another example, this time where the number of marked points, t, is a constant the size distribution has been evaluated for $t=20$. These clumps vary in length from 10 to 20. The parameters a, b and c are given in Table 6.2 from which, by substitution in equation (6.18), the frequency distribution can be calculated. The results for $p=0.2$,

TABLE 6.1. The parameters of the size distribution of clumps length 10 ($s = 10$). Quadratic lattice ($2 \times \infty$)

t	a	b	c
10	2	0	0
11	32	4	0
12	196	60	2
13	584	340	28
14	900	924	146
15	720	1284	360
16	292	924	450
17	56	340	292
18	4	60	98
19	0	4	16
20	0	0	1

0.5 and 0.8, $q=1-p$, are given in Fig. 6.5. At the lowest density ($p=0.2$) the clumps tend to be distributed about the most common length of 14. At $p=0.5$ the most common length is 13 and at the highest density, $p=0.8$, the clumps are very dense and the most common length is 12.

The total number of clumps, which consist of t marked points for all possible values of s, is

$$np^t \sum_s q^{2s-t+2}(a+bq+cq^2) \qquad (6.23)$$

In the one-dimensional case, that is when $m=1$ and n is very large, the total number of clumps is

$$npq$$

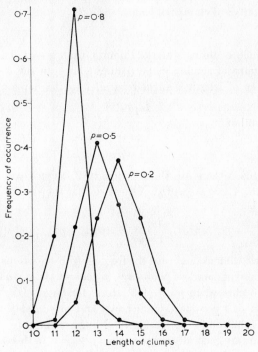

FIG. 6.5. Frequency distribution of the length of clumps of twenty points in a quadratic lattice $2 \times \infty$.

TABLE 6.2. The parameters of the size distribution of clumps of 20 points ($t = 20$)

s	a	b	c
10	0	0	1
11	0	4	128
12	4	2,300	1,556
13	7,060	14,612	5,250
14	25,284	28,732	5,810
15	33,284	22,564	2,720
16	19,844	8,188	578
17	5,876	1,460	56
18	900	124	2
19	68	4	0
20	2	0	0

and the number of clumps of length s is

$$np^s q^2$$

each of which contains s marked points, that is $s=t$. There are, of course, clumps of similar shape (straight lines) in the $2 \times n$ lattice. The number of length s aligned parallel to the horizontal axis is

$$2np^s q^{s+2}$$

giving a total of

$$\frac{2npq^3}{1-pq}$$

and in addition there are those of length 2, aligned parallel to the vertical axis. There are $np^2 q^4$ of these so that the sum total of those of width 1 is

$$np^2 q^4 + \frac{2npq^3}{1-pq} = npq^3(2+pq)$$

In the two-dimensional case the frequency distributions of clumps of length s and of t marked points are, in general, skew. An interesting exception occurs when $p=q=0\cdot5$. Here, for large s, the frequency distribution of t becomes symmetrical and presumably tends to a normal distribution for increasing s, with the mean at $t=\frac{3}{2}s$.

The results are generally simpler when $p+q=1$. In this special case, substituting $q=1-p$

$$A_1 = \frac{2(2+2p-p^2)-(2+p)(1-\sqrt{1+4p-4p^2})}{p(2+p)(1+\sqrt{1+4p-4p^2})\sqrt{1+4p-4p^2}}$$

$$A_2 = \frac{(2+p)(1+\sqrt{1+4p-4p^2})-2(2+2p-p^2)}{p(2+p)(1-\sqrt{1+4p-4p^2})\sqrt{1+4p-4p^2}}$$

and

$$\begin{aligned}
P_s = {}& p^{s-1}\{[2(2+2p-p^2)-(2+p)(1-\sqrt{1+4p-4p^2})]\\
&\times(1+\sqrt{1+4p-4p^2})^{s-1}-[2(2+2p-p^2)\\
&-(2+p)(1+\sqrt{1+4p-4p^2})](1-\sqrt{1+4p-4p^2})^{s-1}\}\\
&\div 2^s(2+p)\sqrt{1+4p-4p^2}
\end{aligned}$$

The lattice $m \times n$; $m=2$, $n=x$, is a very simple one but is the first two-dimensional model completely solved. The complicated nature of the explicit solutions for even this model indicates the size of the mathematical problems yet to be solved.

References

Armitage, P. (1949). *Biometrika*, **36**, 257.
Ashford, J. R., Dodgson, J., Hadden, G. G., Skorobahatyj, B., and Fay, J. W. J. (1963). *Ann. Occup. Hyg.*, **6**, 201.
Beadle, D. G., and Kerrich, J. E. (1955). *J. Chem. Metall. Ming. Soc. S. Afr.*, **56**, 219.
Broadbent, S. R., and Hammersley, J. M. (1957). *Proc. Camb. Phil. Soc.*, **53**, 629.
Cooke-Yarborough, E. H., and Whyard, R. E. (1954). *Brit. J. Appl. Phys.*, Suppl. No. 3, S 147.
Courshee, R. J. (1954). *Brit. J. Appl. Phys.*, Suppl. No. 3, S 161.
Dell, H. A. (1954). *Brit. J. Appl. Phys.*, Suppl. No. 3, S 156.
Domb, E. (1947). *Proc. Camb. Phil. Soc.*, **43**, 329.
Domb, E. (1960). *Advance in Physics*, **9**, 149.
Domb, E., and Sykes, M. F. (1960). *Phys. Rev.*, **122**, 77.
Elliott, R. J., Heap, B. R., Morgan, D. J., and Rushbrooke, G. S. (1960). *Phys. Rev. Letters*, **5**, 366.
Garwood, F. (1947). *Biometrika*, **34**, 1.
Green, H. L., and Watson, H. H. (1935). *Spec. Rep. Ser. med. Res. Coun. (Lond.)*, No. 199.
Gucker, F. T., and Rose, D. G. (1954). *Brit. J. Appl. Phys.*, Suppl. No. 3, S 138.
Hall, P. (1927). *Biometrika*, **19**, 240.
Hamilton, R. J., Holdsworth, M. A., and Walton, W. H. (1954). *Brit. J. Appl. Phys.*, Suppl. No. 3, S 101.
Hammersley, J. (1953). *Proc. Camb. Phil. Soc.*, **49**, 623.
Hammersley, J. (1957a). *Proc. Camb. Phil. Soc.*, **53**, 642.
Hammersley, J. (1957b). *Proc. Camb. Phil. Soc.*, **53**, 790.
Harris, T. E. (1960). *Proc. Camb. Phil. Soc.*, **56**, 13.
Hawkesley, P. G. W. (1954). *Brit. J. Appl. Phys.*, Suppl. No. 3, S 165.
Irwin, J. O., Armitage, P., and Davies, C. N. (1949). *Nature*, 21st May, 809.
Kendall, M. G. (1947). *The Advanced Theory of Statistics*, Vol. 1, p. 240. C. Griffin & Co. Ltd., London.
Kendall, M. G., and Moran, P. A. P. (1963). *Geometrical Probability*. C. Griffin & Co. Ltd., London.
Le Bouffant, L., and Soule, J. L. (1954). *Brit. J. Appl. Phys.*, Suppl. No. 3, S 143.
Lidwell, O. M. (1948). *Studies in Air Hygiene*, Spec. Rep. Ser. med. Res. Coun. No. 262, Appendix V, 341.
Mack, C. (1954). *Proc. Camb. Phil. Soc.*, **50**, 581.
Mack, C. (1955). *Proc. Camb. Phil. Soc.*, **51**, 246.

Martin, G., Blythe, C. E., and Tongue, H. (1923–24). *Trans. Ceram. Soc.*, **23**, 61.

Moran, P. A. P. (1966). *J. Appl. Prob.*, **3**, 453.

National Coal Board (1949). Circular: *The Sampling of Air-borne Dust for the Testing of 'Approved Conditions'*.

Roach, S. A. (1958). *Brit. J. industr. Med.*, **15**, 250.

Roach, S. A. (1959). *Brit. J. industr. Med.*, **16**, 104.

Sato, H., Arrott, A., and Kikuchi, R. (1959). *J. Phys. Chem. Solids*, **10**, 19.

Tanner, J. C. (1951). *Biometrika*, **38**, 383.

Tanner, J. C. (1953). *Biometrika*, **40**, 58.

Watson, H. H. (1936). *Trans. Instn. Ming. and Metall.*, **46**, 176.

Wynn, A. H. A., and Dawes, J. G. (1951). Safety in Mines Research Establishment, Min. Fuel and Power, *Res. Report* No. 28.

Index